Ten Short Stories
From Guided Reading to Autonomy

Françoise Grellet

hachette
ÉDUCATION

Introduction

L'objectif de ce recueil de nouvelles anglaises et américaines est d'encourager la lecture et de mener peu à peu à une lecture autonome, sans aucune aide. C'est pourquoi les nouvelles choisies sont environ de même difficulté tandis que l'aide apportée change peu à peu de nature. Le but d'une fiche de lecture n'est pas seulement d'aider à la lecture d'un texte donné ; c'est aussi de rendre l'élève indépendant, de l'aider à se passer peu à peu de fiche de lecture. La nature de ces fiches doit donc changer au cours de l'apprentissage. C'est ce principe qui est à la base de la progression proposée dans ce livre.

1 Pour les trois premières nouvelles du recueil, la fiche d'accompagnement (To help you with your reading) guide et aide la lecture. Celle-ci est limitée à des passages courts bien définis (une page, puis deux à trois pages) et les questions ont pour but :

- de faire comprendre l'information essentielle nécessaire pour continuer à lire,
- d'aider à inférer, à deviner le sens global des mots, phrases ou paragraphes difficiles.

Cette lecture guidée (sur une trentaine de pages) doit donner confiance face à un texte inconnu, apprendre à ne pas bloquer sur quelques passages obscurs, et prépare donc l'étape suivante.

2 Les trois nouvelles qui suivent devraient être lues sans aucune fiche, pour le plaisir de lire. Mais il peut être rassurant, dans cette phase de l'apprentissage, de vérifier ensuite que les idées principales ont bien été comprises (To check your reading). C'est pourquoi les activités proposées permettent de résumer et de discuter l'information essentielle de chacune de ces nouvelles. Ce travail ne peut que renforcer les réflexes de bonne lecture et conduire à la dernière phase.

3 Les dernières nouvelles proposées sont elles aussi destinées à être lues pour le plaisir. Mais cette fois les idées principales ne sont pas discutées, mais vérifiées indirectement par le biais d'activités d'écriture et d'écoute (After reading the story). Les nouvelles sont en fait utilisées pour d'autres activités de classe et ne seront donc commentées que de façon indirecte.

Nous espérons que ce livre donnera envie de passer à l'étape suivante, celle de la lecture individuelle en dehors de la classe…

hachette s'engage pour
l'environnement en réduisant
l'empreinte carbone de ses livres.
Celle de cet exemplaire est de :

550 g éq. CO$_2$
Rendez-vous sur
www.hachette-durable.fr

PAPIER À BASE DE
FIBRES CERTIFIÉES

Françoise Grellet est professeur de Première supérieure au Lycée Henri IV.

Couverture : Jean-Pierre JAUNEAU
Maquette intérieure : Jean-Pierre JAUNEAU
Réalisation : TYPO-VIRGULE

ISBN : 978-2-01-135181-4
© HACHETTE LIVRE 2000
58, rue Jean Bleuzen, CS 70007, 92178 Vanves Cedex

Sommaire

ROALD DAHL
The Landlady

Billy Weaver had travelled down from London on the slow afternoon train, with a change at Swindon on the way, and by the time he got to Bath it was about nine o'clock in the
5 evening and the moon was coming up out of a clear starry sky over the houses opposite the station entrance. But the air was deadly cold and the wind was like a flat blade of ice on his cheeks.

10 'Excuse me,' he said, 'but is there a fairly cheap hotel not too far away from here?'

'Try The Bell and Dragon,' the porter answered, pointing down the road. 'They might take you in. It's about a quarter of a mile along
15 on the other side.'

Billy thanked him and picked up his suitcase and set out to walk the quarter-mile to The Bell and Dragon. He had never been to Bath before. He didn't know anyone who lived there.
20 But Mr Greenslade at the Head Office in London had told him it was a splendid city. 'Find your own lodgings,' he had said, 'and then go along and report to the Branch Manager as soon as you've got yourself settled.'

25 Billy was seventeen years old. He was wearing a new navy-blue overcoat, a new

brown trilby hat, and a new brown suit, and he was feeling fine. He walked briskly down the street. He was trying to do everything briskly these days. Briskness, he had decided, was *the* one common characteristic of all suc-
30 cessful businessmen. The big shots up at Head Office were absolutely fantastically brisk all the time. They were amazing.

There were no shops on this wide street that he was walking along, only a line of tall houses on each side, all of them identical. They had porches and pillars and four or five steps going up to their front doors, and
35 it was obvious that once upon a time they had been very swanky residences. But now, even in the darkness, he could see that the paint was peeling from the woodwork on their doors and windows, and that the handsome white façades were cracked and blotchy from neglect.

Suddenly, in a downstairs window that was brilliantly illuminated by
40 a street-lamp not six yards away, Billy caught sight of a printed notice propped up against the glass in one of the upper panes. It said BED AND BREAK-FAST. There was a vase of pussy-willows, tall and beautiful, standing just underneath the notice.

He stopped walking. He moved a bit closer. Green curtains (some sort
45 of velvety material) were hanging down on either side of the window. The pussy-willows looked wonderful beside them. He went right up and peered through the glass into the room, and the first thing he saw was a bright fire burning in the hearth. On the carpet in front of the fire, a pretty little dachshund was curled up asleep with its nose tucked into its belly. The room
50 itself, so far as he could see in the half-darkness, was filled with pleasant furniture. There was a baby-grand piano and a big sofa and several plump armchairs; and in one corner he spotted a large parrot in a cage. Animals were usually a good sign in a place like this, Billy told himself; and all in all, it looked to him as though it would be a pretty decent house to stay in.
55 Certainly it would be more comfortable than The Bell and Dragon.

On the other hand, a pub would be more congenial than a boarding-house. There would be beer and darts in the evenings, and lots of people to talk to, and it would probably be a good bit cheaper, too. He had stayed a couple of nights in a pub once before and he had liked it. He had never
60 stayed in any boarding-houses, and, to be perfectly honest, he was a tiny bit frightened of them. The name itself conjured up images of watery cabbage, rapacious landladies, and a powerful smell of kippers in the living-room.

After dithering about like this in the cold for two or three minutes, Billy decided that he would walk on and take a look at The Bell and Dragon
65 before making up his mind. He turned to go.

8

And now a queer thing happened to him. He was in the act of stepping back and turning away from the window when all at once his eye was caught and held in the most peculiar manner by the small notice that was there. BED AND BREAKFAST, it said. BED AND BREAKFAST, BED AND BREAKFAST, 70 BED AND BREAKFAST. Each word was like a large black eye staring at him through the glass, holding him, compelling him, forcing him to stay where he was and not to walk away from that house, and the next thing he knew, he was actually moving across from the window to the front door of the house, climbing the steps that led up to it, and reaching for the bell.

75   He pressed the bell. Far away in a back room he heard it ringing, and then *at once* – it must have been at once because he hadn't even had time to take his finger from the bell-button – the door swung open and a woman was standing there.

Normally you ring the bell and you have at least a half-minute's wait 80 before the door opens. But this dame was like a jack-in-the-box. He pressed the bell – and out she popped! It made him jump.

She was about forty-five or fifty years old, and the moment she saw him, she gave him a warm welcoming smile.

'*Please* come in,' she said pleasantly. She stepped aside, holding the 85 door wide open, and Billy found himself automatically starting forward into the house. The compulsion or, more accurately, the desire to follow after her into that house was extraordinarily strong.

'I saw the notice in the window,' he said, holding himself back.

'Yes, I know.'

90   'I was wondering about a room.'

'It's, *all* ready for you, my dear,' she said. She had a round pink face and very gentle blue eyes.

'I was on my way to The Bell and Dragon,' Billy told her. 'But the notice in your window just happened to catch my eye.'

95   'My dear boy,' she said, 'why don't you come in out of the cold?'

'How much do you charge?'

'Five and sixpence[1] a night, including breakfast.'

It was fantastically cheap. It was less than half of what he had been willing to pay.

100   'If that is too much,' she added, 'then perhaps I can reduce it just a tiny bit. Do you desire an egg for breakfast? Eggs are expensive at the moment. It would be sixpence less without the egg.'

---

1. Five and sixpence = five shillings and six pence.

'Five and sixpence is fine,' he answered. 'I should like very much to stay here.'

'I knew you would. Do come in.'

She seemed terribly nice. She looked exactly like the mother of one's best school-friend welcoming one into the house to stay for the Christmas holidays. Billy took off his hat, and stepped over the threshold.

'Just hang it there,' she said, 'and let me help you with your coat.'

110 There were no other hats or coats in the hall. There were no umbrellas, no walking-sticks – nothing.

'We have it *all* to ourselves,' she said, smiling at him over her shoulder as she led the way upstairs. 'You see, it isn't very often I have the pleasure of taking a visitor into my little nest.'

115 The old girl is slightly dotty, Billy told himself. But at five and sixpence a night, who gives a damn about that? 'I should've thought you'd be simply swamped with applicants,' he said politely.

'Oh, I am, my dear, I am, of course I am. But the trouble is that I'm inclined to be just a teeny weeny bit choosy and particular – if you see what 120 I mean.'

'Ah, yes.'

'But I'm always ready. Everything is always ready day and night in this house just on the off-chance that an acceptable young gentleman will come along. And it is such a pleasure, my dear, such a very great pleasure 125 when now and again I open the door and I see someone standing there who is just *exactly* right.' She was half-way up the stairs, and she paused with one hand on the stair-rail, turning her head and smiling down at him with pale lips. 'Like you,' she added, and her blue eyes travelled slowly all the way down the length of Billy's body, to his feet, and then up 130 again.

On the first-floor landing she said to him, 'This floor is mine.'

They climbed up a second flight. 'And this one is *all* yours,' she said. 'Here's your room. I do hope you'll like it.' She took him into a small but charming front bedroom, switching on the light as she went in.

135 'The morning sun comes right in the window, Mr Perkins. It *is* Mr Perkins, isn't it?'

'No,' he said, 'It's Weaver.'

'Mr Weaver. How nice. I've put a water-bottle between the sheets to air them out, Mr Weaver. It's such a comfort to have a hot water-bottle in 140 a strange bed with clean sheets, don't you agree? And you may light the gas fire at any time if you feel chilly.'

10

'Thank you,' Billy said. 'Thank you ever so much.' He noticed that the bedspread had been taken off the bed, and that the bedclothes had been neatly turned back on one side, all ready for someone to get in.

145 'I'm so glad you appeared,' she said, looking earnestly into his face. 'I was beginning to get worried.'

'That's all right,' Billy answered brightly. 'You mustn't worry about me.' He put his suitcase on the chair and started to open it.

'And what about supper, my dear? Did you manage to get anything 150 to eat before you came here?'

'I'm not a bit hungry, thank you,' he said. 'I think I'll just go to bed as soon as possible because tomorrow I've got to get up rather early and report to the office.'

'Very well, then. I'll leave you now so that you can unpack. But 155 before you go to bed, would you be kind enough to pop into the sitting-room on the ground floor and sign the book? Everyone has to do that because it's the law of the land, and we don't want to go breaking any laws at *this* stage of the proceedings, do we?' She gave him a little wave of the hand and went quickly out of the room and closed the door.

160 Now, the fact that his landlady appeared to be slightly off her rocker didn't worry Billy in the least. After all, she was not only harmless – there was no question about that – but she was also quite obviously a kind and generous soul. He guessed that she had probably lost a son in the war, or something like that, and had never got over it.

165 So a few minutes later, after unpacking his suitcase and washing his hands, he trotted downstairs to the ground floor and entered the living-room. His landlady wasn't there, but the fire was glowing in the hearth, and the little dachshund was still sleeping in front of it. The room was wonderfully warm and cosy. I'm a lucky fellow, he thought, rubbing his hands. This is a bit of all right.

170 He found the guest-book lying open on the piano, so he took out his pen and wrote down his name and address. There were only two other entries above his on the page, and, as one always does with guest-books, he started to read them. One was a Christopher Mulholland from Cardiff. The other was Gregory W. Temple from Bristol.

175 That's funny, he thought suddenly. Christopher Mulholland. It rings a bell.

Now where on earth had he heard that rather unusual name before?

Was he a boy at school? No. Was it one of his sister's numerous young men, perhaps, or a friend of his father's? No, no, it wasn't any of those. He 180 glanced down again at the book.

| Christopher Mulholland | 231 Cathedral Road, Cardiff |
| Gregory W. Temple | 27 Sycamore Drive, Bristol |

As a matter of fact, now he came to think of it, he wasn't at all sure that the second name didn't have almost as much of a familiar ring about it as the first.

'Gregory Temple?' he said aloud, searching his memory. 'Christopher Mulholland?...'

'Such charming boys,' a voice behind him answered, and he turned and saw his landlady sailing into the room with a large silver tea-tray in her hands. She was holding it well out in front of her, and rather high up, as though the tray were a pair of reins on a frisky horse.

'They sound somehow familiar,' he said.

'They do? How interesting.'

'I'm almost positive I've heard those names before somewhere. Isn't that queer? Maybe it was in the newspapers. They weren't famous in any way, were they? I mean famous cricketers or footballers or something like that?'

'Famous,' she said, setting the tea-tray down on the low table in front of the sofa. 'Oh no, I don't think they were famous. But they were extraordinarily handsome, both of them, I can promise you that. They were tall and young and handsome, my dear, just exactly like you.'

Once more, Billy glanced down at the book. 'Look here,' he said, noticing the dates. 'This last entry is over two years old.'

'It is?'

'Yes, indeed. And Christopher Mulholland's is nearly a year before that – more than *three years* ago.'

'Dear me,' she said, shaking her head and heaving a dainty little sigh. 'I would never have thought it. How time does fly away from us all, doesn't it, Mr Wilkins?'

'Its Weaver,' Billy said. 'W-e-a-v-e-r.'

'Oh, of course it is!' she cried, sitting down on the sofa. 'How silly of me. I do apologize. In one ear and out the other, that's me, Mr Weaver.'

'You know something?' Billy said. 'Something that's really quite extraordinary about all this?'

'No, dear, I don't.'

'Well, you see – both of these names, Mulholland and Temple, I not only seem to remember each one of them separately, so to speak, but somehow or other, in some peculiar way, they both appear to be sort of connected together as well. As though they were both famous for the same sort of thing, if you see what I mean – like… well… like Dempsey and Tunney, for example, or Churchill and Roosevelt.'

'How amusing,' she said. 'but come over here now, dear, and sit down beside me on the sofa and I'll give you a nice cup of tea and a ginger biscuit before you go to bed.'

'You really shouldn't bother,' Billy said. 'I didn't mean you to do anything like that.' He stood by the piano, watching her as she fussed about with the cups and saucers. He noticed that she had small, white, quickly moving hands, and red finger-nails.

'I'm almost positive it was in the newspapers I saw them,' Billy said. 'I'll think of it in a second. I'm sure I will.'

There is nothing more tantalizing than a thing like this which lingers just outside the borders of one's memory. He hated to give up.

'Now wait a minute,' he said, 'Wait just a minute. Mulholland… Christopher Mulholland… wasn't *that* the name of the Eton schoolboy who was on a walking-tour through the West Country, and then all of a sudden…

'Milk?' she said. 'And sugar?'

'Yes, please. And then all of a sudden…'

'Eton schoolboy?' she said. 'Oh no, my dear, that can't possibly be right because *my* Mr Mulholland was certainly not an Eton schoolboy when he came to me. He was a Cambridge undergraduate. Come over here now and sit next to me and warm yourself in front of this lovely fire. Come on. Your tea's all ready for you.' She patted the empty place beside her on the sofa, and she sat there smiling at Billy and waiting for him to come over.

He crossed the room slowly, and sat down on the edge of the sofa. She placed his teacup on the table in front of him.

'*There* we are,' she said. 'How nice and cosy this is, isn't it?'

Billy started sipping his tea. She did the same. For half a minute or so, neither of them spoke. But Billy knew that she was looking at him. Her body was half-turned towards him, and he could feel her eyes resting on his face, watching him over the rim of her teacup. Now and again, he caught a whiff of a peculiar smell that seemed to emanate directly from her person. It was not in the least unpleasant, and it reminded him – well, he wasn't quite sure what it reminded him of. Pickled walnuts? New leather? Or was it the corridors of a hospital?

'Mr Mulholland was a great one for his tea,' she said at length. 'Never in my life have I seen anyone drink as much tea as dear, sweet Mr Mulholland.'

'I suppose he left fairly recently,' Billy said. He was still puzzling his
260 head about the two names. He was positive now that he had seen them in
the newspapers – in the headlines.

'Left?' she said, arching her brows. 'But my dear boy, he never left.
He's still here. Mr Temple is also here. They're on the third floor, both of
them together.'

265   Billy set down his cup slowly on the table, and stared at his landlady.
She smiled back at him, and then she put out one of her white hands and
patted him comfortingly on the knee. 'How old are you, my dear?' she asked.

'Seventeen.'

'Seventeen!' she cried. 'Oh, it's the perfect age! Mr Mulholland was
270 also seventeen. But I think he was a trifle shorter than you are, in fact I'm
sure he was, and his teeth weren't *quite* so white. You have the most beautiful teeth, Mr Weaver, did you know that?'

'They're not as good as they look,' Billy said. 'They've got simply
masses of fillings in them at the back.'

275   'Mr Temple, of course, was a little older,' she said, ignoring his
remark. 'He was actually twenty-eight. And yet I never would have guessed
it if he hadn't told me, never in my whole life. There wasn't a *blemish* on
his body.'

'A what?' Billy said.

280   'His skin was *just* like a baby's.'

There was a pause. Billy picked up his teacup and took another sip
of his tea, then he set it down again gently in its saucer. He waited for her
to say something else, but she seemed to have lapsed into another of her
silences. He sat there staring straight ahead of him into the far corner of
285 the room, biting his lower lip.

'That parrot,' he said at last. 'You know something? It had me completely fooled when I first saw it through the window from the street. I
could have sworn it was alive.'

'Alas, no longer.'

290   'It's most terribly clever the way it's been done,' he said. 'It doesn't
look in the least bit dead. Who did it?'

'I did.'

'*You* did?'

'Of course,' she said. 'And you have met my little Basil as well?' She
295 nodded towards the dachshund curled up so comfortably in front of the
fire. Billy looked at it. And suddenly, he realized that this animal had all the
time been just as silent and motionless as the parrot. He put out a hand and

14

touched it gently on the top of its back. The back was hard and cold, and when he pushed the hair to one side with his fingers, he could see the skin
300 underneath, greyish-black and dry and perfectly preserved.

'Good gracious me,' he said. 'How absolutely fascinating.' He turned away from the dog and stared with deep admiration at the little woman beside him on the sofa. 'It must be most awfully difficult to do a thing like that.'

305 'Not in the least,' she said. 'I stuff *all* my little pets myself when they pass away. Will you have another cup of tea?'

'No, thank you,' Billy said. The tea tasted faintly of bitter almonds, and he didn't much care for it.

'You did sign the book, didn't you?'

310 'Oh, yes.'

'That's good. Because later on, if I happen to forget what you were called, then I can always come down here and look it up. I still do that almost every day with Mr Mulholland and Mr... Mr...'

'Temple,' Billy said, 'Gregory Temple. Excuse my asking, but haven't
315 there been *any* other guests here except them in the last two or three years?'

Holding her teacup high in one hand, inclining her head slightly to the left, she looked up at him out of the corners of her eyes and gave him another gentle little smile.

320 'No, my dear,' she said. 'Only you.'

ROALD DAHL (1916-1990)
was born in Wales, to Norwegian parents. He served
as a fighter pilot during the war, then started his career
as a writer. He is best-known for his children's books (for example,
Charlie and the Chocolate Factory) and his short stories,
which are clever and well-crafted, full of suspense and
dark humour, and which often have surprise endings.

Short Stories:
Someone Like You (1953)
Kiss, Kiss (1959)
Switch Bitch (1974)

1 **Read the beginning of this short story by Roald Dahl, down to "from neglect" (l. 38). Read the whole passage even if there are words or sentences you do not understand. Then answer the following questions.**

A. What do we learn at the beginning of the story?

It is about:
1. a young man who is looking for a pub in London.
2. a young man who is looking for a place to stay in Bath.
3. a young man who is cold and tired because of a long train journey.

Billy has come there:
1. to make new friends.
2. to take on a new job.
3. to find lodgings.

The houses along the street:
1. are in good condition.
2. are no longer lived in.
3. are in need of repair.

B. List all the information you are given about Billy:

– Name: ....

– Age: ....

– Job: ....

– Place of work: before: .... now: ....

– Any further information? ....

....

C. Match the following expressions and what they refer to:

a. The Bell and Dragon (l. 12) (A) the principal office of a business
b. The Head Office (l. 20) (B) the director of a subdivision of the same business
c. The Branch Manager (l. 23) (C) a pub

D. Can you infer the meaning and word-class (e.g. adjective, verb, preposition...?) of the following words and expressions? What elements in the context helped you find out?

WORDS / EXPRESSIONS	WORD-CLASS	MEANING
settled (l. 24)		
briskly (l. 28)		
big shots (l. 30)		
swanky (l. 35)		

16

2 Now continue reading in the same way, down to "reaching for the bell" (l. 74). Then answer the following questions.

A. Find the main information you learn in this passage.

The bed and breakfast place:
1. looks lovely and comfortable.
2. has too much furniture and too many animals.
3. does not appeal to Billy.

Billy decides:
1. that a pub is better than a B&B (= Bed & Breakfast).
2. that this B&B is better.
3. that he must see The Bell and Dragon before deciding.

Billy reaches for the bell of the B&B because:
1. he suddenly understands he will be better there.
2. he likes the letters of the words B&B.
3. he feels obliged to go there without knowing why.

B. Billy mentally compares what he knows of B&Bs and pubs. Underline:
- three of the advantages of pubs for him;
- three of the advantages of B&Bs for him.

Now look again at the paragraph in which you find this comparison and try to infer the overall meaning of the following words. What elements helped you decide?

– congenial (l. 56): ....

– darts (l. 57): ....

– cabbage (l. 61): ....

– kippers (l. 62): ....

C. List all the elements which:

MAKE THE B&B BILLY SEES THROUGH THE WINDOW A PLEASANT PLACE.	MAKE THE B&B SEEM STRANGE AT THE END OF THE PASSAGE.
– plant:	– synonyms of "strange":
– animals:	– strange comparison:
– furniture:	– verbs showing Billy cannot control his actions:
– adjectives with pleasant connotations:	

Can you imagine how the story will develop from now on? Suggest different possibilities.

3 Read the text down to "This is a bit of all right." (l. 169)
Then answer the following questions.

A. Billy has now entered the B&B. What rooms and places does he find himself in, chronologically?

– ....

– ....

– ....

– ....

B. List all the elements that:

ARE STRANGE OR UNUSUAL ABOUT THE B&B.	SHOW THAT THE LANDLADY IS WELCOMING.
–	–
–	–
–	–
–	–
–	–
–	–

C. Using the context, can you infer the meaning of the following words and expressions?

– dotty (l. 115): ....

– swamped with applicants (l. 117): ....

– off her rocker (l. 160): ....

4 Read the end of the story, then answer the following questions.

A. The guest-book

– How many names are mentioned in it? ....

....

– What are they? ....

– What does Billy associate them with? ....

– How long ago did they come to the B&B? ....

....

– What words does the landlady use to speak of them? ....

....

B. Now that you have read the story, can you guess what happened to the other two guests and what is going to happen to Billy?

....

....

....

....

Now look at the "disturbing" details below and explain in what way they announce and explain what will take place (even though Billy is not yet aware that something is wrong).

DISTURBING ELEMENTS	HOW YOU CAN EXPLAIN THEM
The landlady's smell.	
C. Mulholland and G. Temple are still on the third floor.	
The landlady has seen their naked bodies.	
She stuffed the parrot and the dog.	
The tea tastes of bitter almonds.	
The landlady wants to remember Billy's name later on.	

5 Imagine the story has one more page. Write it.

or:

Billy mentions an item of news about Christopher Mulholland. Write the newspaper article that will be published after Billy's disappearance.

6 A closer look at language

IN THE STORY

**Here are some sentences from the short story.
Justify the use of the tenses in them.**

a. He had never been to Bath before. (l. 18-19)

b. "I'm almost positive I've heard those names before somewhere." (l. 194)

c. There is nothing more tantalizing than a thing like this which lingers just outside the borders of one's memory. He hated to give up. (l. 231-232)

d. He crossed the room slowly, and sat down on the edge of the sofa. (l. 245)

e. "He was actually twenty-eight. And yet I never would have guessed it if he hadn't told me..." (l. 276-277)

f. "Excuse my asking, but haven't there been *any* other guests here except them in the last two or three years?" (l. 314-316)

FURTHER PRACTICE

**Complete the following sentences with the verbs given
between parentheses, using the right tense and verb form
(present / past / present perfect / past perfect / conditional).**

a. "I .... such beautifully preserved animals," he said. (see + never)

b. Billy .... the station and .... looking for a pub. (leave / start)

c. "I .... if I hadn't seen the sign," he said. (stop + not)

d. Billy .... in a pub before and .... it. (stay + once / like)

e. "I .... from London," Billy explained to the landlady. (arrive + just)

f. It .... well-known that landladies .... rarely generous, and Billy therefore .... staying in a pub. (be / prefer)

g. Billy thought that if he stayed in the B&B, it .... more comfortable and cheaper. (be)

h. All this time, the dog .... as quiet and motionless as the parrot. (be)

20

Notes

TONY WILMOT

Skeleton in the Cupboard[1]

He was watching the park gates from his usual bench by the pond. The girl would soon be joining him for her mid-day break.

For several days now they had sat at the
5 same bench and exchanged pleasantries after she had laughed at the way the ducks fought over the crusts he had thrown to them.

She was twenty-ish, attractive, with a pulse-quickening figure, but he did not flatter
10 himself that her interest was in any way sexual. He subscribed to the adage 'No fool like an old fool'. Besides, he was more than twice her age.

To him it was a harmless flirtation – a
15 fillip to his middle-aged man's morale – and he had found himself looking forward to their lunchtime 'assignations'.

Earlier that morning, however, events had taken a more serious turn. The girl had paid
20 a visit to the Vehicle Registration Department in the Town Hall.

His secretary had come into his office. 'There's a young lady here, Mr Smythe, asking if

1. Skeleton in the Cupboard: you have a skeleton in the cupboard when you say nothing to other people about something unpleasant or embarrassing in your life.

we keep records of car ownership... MG sports cars in particular. I said I
25 thought not.'

He had felt a twinge of unease at the mention of the car type.

'Quite so,' he had replied. 'Tell her registrations are all on the natio-
nal computer now. In any case, we couldn't give out that kind of information.'

30 He had peered at the reception desk through his office's glass parti-
tion. The enquirer was the girl from the park bench.

An odd coincidence, he had thought. Or was it something more?

Now, as she entered the park gates with that long stride and purposeful
expression, his unease returned.

35 'Hello – we meet again,' she said, sitting beside him.

'Ah, yes... sky looks a bit overcast. Hope we aren't in for some rain.'
He gestured at the apple she was peeling with a penknife. 'Lunch?'

'Yes, worse luck. I'm on a diet.'

He smiled. 'You seem to be here most days. Do you work hereabouts?'

40 'Oh no. In fact, I don't live here. I'm just staying in town while I'm
doing some research. I'm from Elmston, actually.'

'Really? I know Elmston...' he began. The words were out before the
warning bell rang. 'Well, I don't exactly know it... pal of mine... knew him
years ago... used to live there. Is this your first visit here?'

45 'Yes.'

'Nice place,' he said. 'Bit dull, though.'

'Not at all. It's charming.'

'What are you researching? Our town's chequered[2] history, perhaps?
Parts date from the Roman occupation.'

50 'How interesting. But no – I'm trying to trace someone.'

'Ah! Bit of detective work?'

She smiled. 'In a way. I'm beginning to find out what a job it is tracing someone who may not want to be traced. No wonder the police have
to spend so much time on investigations.'

55 'And the "trail" has led from Elmston to here?'

'Indirectly, yes, But I've had to spend time in several places first. I'm
hoping this will be the last.'

'Sounds very intriguing,' he said, hoping to entice her to reveal more
without seeming to be prying into her private life.

---

2. Chequered: with good and bad times in it.

24

60 　'I suppose it is, in a way. I'm going back more than twenty years, though.' She made a wry face. 'Which is setting myself a difficult task.'

'I don't suppose you were even born then?' he said.

'I was – just! Anyway, I've managed to unearth a few clues. The person I'm looking for had an MG sports car then and got married during the 65 same period. I know it's a bit of a long shot, but it might just pay off.'

His unease became a shiver which set him on edge even more. He was like the rabbit hypnotized by the snake, wanting to get away but unable to move. 'But I mustn't bore you with my personal affairs,' she went on. 'What about you? What line of business are you in?'

70 　'Oh, nothing much. Civil servant, actually. Quite dull, I'm afraid. I wish I could be an 007 like you but… I'm just a nine-to-five chap.'

'Don't be so modest. There's nothing wrong with being a civil servant.'

He made a deprecating gesture but inwardly he was thrilled that a pretty girl was finding him interesting enough to want to flirt with him.

75 　'Married, of course?'

He was on the point of saying no when he noticed her glance at the ring on his left hand. He nodded.

'The dishy men always are! Lived here long, have you?'

He did not like the turn the conversation was taking. 'Oh, quite some 80 time.' He made a show of checking his wristwatch. 'Well, I must be getting back. The grindstone[3] waits for no man! I, er… that is, perhaps we might see each other again tomorrow?'

'Yes, let's. About one o'clock?'

He said that would be fine.

85 As he walked back to the Town Hall doubts and fears scurried around his head like cornered rats. It was just too damned close to be coincidence any more. For *he* used to run an MG. And *he* had married twenty years ago.

He could not concentrate at the office. An hour before finishing time, he got his car from the staff car-park and drove to his semi[4] in a leafy 90 suburb on the outskirts of town.

Margaret, his wife, was doing some work in the garden. 'Robert, is that you? You're early. Nothing wrong at the office, is there?'

'No, of course not.' Why did women always think the worst? 'I thought I'd finish off that lampstand in the shed while there's still some day-95 light.'

---

3. Grindstone: from the expression "to keep your nose to the grindstone" = to work very hard.

4. Semi: semi-detached house.

'Right-o! I'll call you when dinner's ready.'

He put the inside catch on the shed door and made sure his wife was still in the front garden. Then he got a metal box from behind his workbench.

100 The key to the box was hidden under a bottle of weedkiller. Inside the box were two yellowing clippings from the *Elmston Observer.*

One was headlined: *Girl, 10, killed in hit-and-run.*

For the umpteenth time[5] he read how the girl had been knocked down on a pedestrian crossing while on her way home from a school 105 friend's house.

The details were embedded in his memory. He had driven over to Margaret's parents' house in the MG that evening. They had lived just outside Elmston then.

Because of some road works, the traffic had been diverted.

110 He had been exceeding the speed limit, too. It was an unfamiliar route and the crossing had taken him by surprise.

The car's brakes were slack because he'd skipped a service to save money, and a shower had made the road surface slippery...

Even though it was twenty years ago, he could still remember the 115 sickening thud... the scream... the crumpled body on the side of the road.

Of course, he should have stopped, but he had panicked. He had been short-listed for a new job for which a clean driving licence was a condition of employment and it was only days away from his wedding. Reporting the accident would have ruined everything.

120 The second clipping, headed *Police appeal for witnesses,* said several people had heard the screech of brakes but none had seen the accident.

A police spokesman was quoted as saying they were 'pursuing several lines of enquiry'.

He locked the clippings away again and returned the box to its 125 hiding place. He had never fully understood why he had kept them all those years. What, he wondered, would the psychologists make of that? A guilt complex, perhaps? A subconscious desire to punish himself for his crime?

It was his favourite tuna-fish salad for dinner but the memory of the accident had dulled his appetite. He pecked away at it, nodding absently as 130 Margaret related the events of her day.

All through the meal the thought kept hammering in his brain: how long before the girl found out that *he* was the hit-and-run driver?

---

5. The umpteenth time : *la énième fois.*

26

More than likely she was a former schoolfriend wanting to see just-ice done. Or a relative… the dead girl's sister, even.

135 The police enquiries had no doubt fizzled out years ago – they would have had far more pressing cases on their plate – but the little girl's family and friends would not have given up the search.

That night he hardly slept. At the office next day he clockwatched until it was time to go to the park. The girl was already there when he arrived.

140 'I was hoping I'd see you today,' she said. 'You see, I'm certain I've come to the right town. You know I mentioned an MG… well, how's this for amateur sleuthing?… There's the car's number.'

A muscle in his cheek began to twitch rapidly as he read what was in her notebook. *His* MG's number. But how had she…? The newspaper 145 report said there had been no eyewitnesses.

'I'm missing the middle one or two digits in the numberplate – but it's enough.'

'Very cloak-and-daggerish[6]' he said, forcing a smile. 'Have you tried the local Vehicle Registration Department? Perhaps they can help.'

150 'Oh yes. No luck, though. But guess what – I've got a photograph of the car.'

The park seemed to spin. He gripped the bench with both hands.

'You all right?' she asked.

'What? Oh yes. Just a twinge of indigestion.'

155 'Well, I haven't actually got the photograph,' she went on. 'I've only seen the negative. I'm having a ten-by-eight print done from it.'

'You have been busy!' His voice sounded unreal. 'Look, that friend of mine from Elmston. I've just remembered. *He* had an MG. He could be who you are looking for… I might still have an address for him at home… Have 160 you got a phone number where I can contact you? Better still, an address in case I miss you here tomorrow.'

She wrote down both in her notebook and tore the page out for him. 'Now I must be off,' she said. 'I've got more sleuthing to do. I'll look out for you here again tomorrow.'

165 He gave her a minute or two's start, then began to follow her.

Her first stop was at a photographic shop near the main square. She came out carrying a large buff-coloured envelope.

That would be the MG print, he thought, as he observed her getting her bearings.

---

6. Cloak-and-daggerish: a cloak-and-dagger situation is secret and mysterious.

170 He kept about fifty yards behind as she crossed the town centre to the offices of the *Evening Gazette.*

He followed her through the revolving doors, keeping the public newspaper stands in the foyer between himself and the point where she was talking at the enquiry counter.

175 Pretending to leaf through the week's back numbers, he could hear snatches of conversation above the din of typewriters and telephones.

'... wedding report twenty-one years ago... would it be possible to...'

'... archives are on the fourth floor... first door on the right as you come out of the lift...'

180 He watched the girl take the lift. Time passed. People came and went. He felt clammy and conspicuous.

Eventually she reappeared out of the lift. The receptionist smiled. Had she found what she had been looking for?

Yes, she had.

185 He was in a cold sweat now, but he had no difficulty keeping her in sight, for he knew the town like the back of his hand. Where would she head next? Oh God, he thought, don't let it be the police station.

'Robert! Long time no see!' He started. It was a man he knew from the Parks Department. He felt like a schoolboy caught playing truant.
190 'Stretching your legs, eh, Robert?'

'Oh, er, yes.' He could see the girl disappearing down a side turning. 'Popped out for cigarettes.'

The man was grinning. 'Some looker, eh?'

'What?'

195 'That girl you were staring at.'

'Oh,' he forced a smile. 'Look, can't stop now. Let's have a drink next week. I'll ring you.'

When he finally got away, the girl was nowhere to be seen. He spent the rest of the afternoon fretting at his desk. Whose wedding had she loo-
200 ked up? And why?

It was not until he and Margaret were watching TV that evening that the answer came to him; in fact, it was staring him in the face...

On the piano was an ornately framed picture of him and Margaret on their wedding day. Of course! Why hadn't he thought of it sooner? The
205 other photos in the family album: there was one of the MG.

He found the album and flicked through it. There is was – the pair of them, snapped in the MG as they were leaving the reception to go off on honeymoon.

28

He stared at himself from twenty years ago: thin face, unlined, thick
210 curling hair. Now he had a double chin, was balding, wore a moustache and
bifocals. Unrecognizable!

On the back of the MG was a 'Just married' placard, which obscured
the middle two digits on the rear numberplate.

The girl must have gone to every photographer in the district until
215 she found the one who had taken their wedding pictures. The negatives
would have been on file, probably in a storeroom.

The girl had got a print. Then she had searched the *Evening
Gazette's* back issues for the paper's own picture of the same couple in the
MG... which would tell her the names and parents' addresses.

220 And there the search would stop, for Margaret's parents had emi-
grated long ago and his own parents were dead. He was safe.

Then it struck him like a blow. 'The electoral roll,' he said out loud.
'She simply goes through it, street by street, until she finds my name...'

'Did you say something, Robert?' Margaret called.

225 'What? No, nothing.'

It would be only a matter of time now before his skeleton was out
of its cupboard. He would be branded a child-killer, all the more heinous
because he had covered his tracks (he had sold the MG immediately they
had got back from honeymoon).

230 He would get at least five years for manslaughter. He would lose his
job; his reputation would be ruined; everything he had built up over the
years... down the drain!

He knew he had not got the strength of character to begin all over
again; he was too set in his ways...

235 'I think I'll go to The Swan for a pint, love. Don't wait up. I might be
late.'

'Oh, all right. I'll leave something out for your supper.'

At times like this, he mused, it was positively an advantage having a
conventionally predictable spouse.

240 It was a fifteen-minute drive to the block of service flats where the girl was
staying; hers was on the ground floor.

She came to the door in a dressing-gown with a towel wrapped
round her hair.

He was sorry to barge in on her unannounced, he blurted; but he
245 had found himself in the neighbourhood, so he had thought he would give
her that information about his friend.

'Oh, well, come in. You'll have to forgive my appearance – I'm in the middle of washing my hair. Can I get you a drink?'

'I won't, thanks – I'm driving.'

250   'Ah yes... the old breathalyser!

'He tried to smile but couldn't move his face muscles. 'That friend,' he began, swallowing. 'His name's... Smythe... Robert Smythe.'

'That's it,' she cried. 'The same one I've been looking for! I found his address this afternoon, in the electoral roll at the Town Hall.'

255   So it was true, he thought; she *was* tracking him down.

'Perhaps I will have that drink,' he said, slipping a hand into his jacket pocket.

She was at the drinks cabinet, her back to him. 'Gin and tonic all right?'

260   'Fine.' He pulled out a length of cord. It went round her neck so easily. He did not make a sound as he pulled it tight. Nor did she...

At the breakfast table next morning Margaret thought Robert looked pale and drawn; there were dark rings round his eyes and he seemed unusually preoccupied. Clearly he needed a holiday; he was working far too hard at
265 that office.

She knew it probably would not be much good urging him to take the day off but she decided to try; to her surprise, he agreed.

'I do have a bit of a migraine, love,' he said.

'The rest will do you good. I'll ring the office and tell them you're
270 not well.'

The 'plop' on the mat inside the front door told her the post had arrived. 'I'll go,' she said.

Two letters. One was Robert's bank statement, the other was for her. An unfamiliar handwriting.

275   She tore it open on her way back to the kitchen. It was a three-page letter, with a snapshot. The sudden shock, as she began to read, made her giddy.

      *... all I had to go on was your maiden name... you'd be surprised how many Margarets with that surname have got married since I was
280 born... it meant checking each one to find if it was the right Margaret...*

She stared at the attractive, fair-haired girl in the snap. Could it be... after all these years? It was something she had buried in her memory, some-

30

thing she had thought would remain buried; but, deep down, hadn't she
285 always known she would never be able to escape from her past?

... when I first learned the truth about myself, I was hurt and angry
... but now that I'm grown up myself, I'm able to understand why you did
what you did...

She sat at the table and rested her hands on the scrubbed pine to
290 stop them from trembling. She glanced at Robert but he seemed unaware
of her agitation.

...finally traced you through your mariage to Robert Smythe... and
now I feel I must meet you... of course, my adoptive parents will always be
'Mum' and 'Dad' to me but...

295   Blinking back the tears, she heard Robert asking if the letter was bad
news.
      'Bad? Oh no...' Quite the contrary, she thought. But how would her
husband take it?
      The guilt she had borne all those years suddenly overwhelmed her
300 and she pushed the snapshot across the table.
      'Robert, I don't quite know how to... there's something I've got to
tell you... something that happened before I met you...'

1 **Read down to "Or was it something more?" (l. 32) Then answer the following questions.**

A. The main information you learn in the passage.

The narrator and the girl:
1. are having an affair.
2. meet for lunch in the park.
3. discuss car registrations.

The girl:
1. owns an MG car.
2. is looking for the owner of an MG car.
3. wants to buy an MG car.

This:
1. worries
2. surprises } the narrator.
3. amuses

B. A few facts: what do you learn about the man and the girl in this passage?

	The man	The girl
Name		
Age		
Profession		

C. How can you infer the general meaning of the following words and expressions? Look carefully at the context before making your guesses. Can the way the words are built sometimes help you?

– a fillip (l. 15): (is it something positive? negative?) ....

– keep records (l. 24): ....

– a twinge of unease (l. 26): ....

– enquirer (l. 31): ....

2 **Now continue reading, down to "He said that would be fine."(l. 84) Then answer the following questions.**

A. What you learn about the girl:

– Where she lives: ....

– What she is doing now: ....

– What she knows about the person she is looking for: ....

....

B. The man's reaction to what she says: list all the expressions showing his growing worry.

....

C. Now, anticipate: How can you explain the man's reaction? Imagine what could have happened earlier in his life.

D. The vocabulary of detection.

1. Find the words which, in the text, correspond to the following meanings (this is the order in which they appear):

– trying to find someone: ....

– police research: ....

– information you gather to find someone: ....

– to discover something: ....

– signs, elements that help you solve a problem: ....

2. Can you infer the general meaning of the following words or expressions?

– stride (l. 33): ....

– overcast (l. 36): ....

– pal of mine (l. 43): ....

– prying into (l. 59): ....

– deprecating (l. 73): ....

– dishy (l. 78): ....

3 Continue reading, down to "staring him in the face..." (l. 202) Then answer the following questions.

A. The events of twenty years ago:

What?	
Where?	
When?	
Why?	

The man's reaction then:

What?
Why?

B. The girl's investigations: what new information has she learnt?

....

....

What information do you think she gets from the *Evening Gazette*?

....

4 **Read the end of the story and write one of the following.**

– The whole of the letter Margaret receives.

– The newspaper article written after the discovery of the girl's body.

– The conversation which takes place at the very end of the story between Robert and Margaret.

5 A closer look at language

IN THE STORY

Underline the modals in the following sentences from the story, then explain why they are used.

1. "I'm beginning to find out what a job it is tracing someone who may not want to be traced." (l. 52-53)

2. "But I mustn't bore you with my personal affairs," she went on. (l. 68)

3. "Well, I must be getting back. The grindstone waits for no man!" (l. 80-81)

4. "... perhaps we might see each other again tomorrow?" (l. 81-82)

5. He could not concentrate at the office. (l. 88)

6. Even though it was twenty years ago, he could still remember the sickening thud... (l. 114-115)

7. Of course, he should have stopped, but he had panicked. (l. 116)

8. "Look, that friend of mine from Elmston. I've just remembered. *He* had an MG. He could be who you are looking for... I might still have an address for him at home... Have you got a phone number where I can contact you?" (l. 157-160)

9. That would be the MG print, he thought... (l. 168)

10. ... he could hear snatches of conversation above the din of typewriters and telephones. (l. 175-176)

11. The girl must have gone to every photographer in the district until she found the one who had taken their wedding pictures. (l. 214-215)

12. "I think I'll go to the Swan for a pint, love. Don't wait up. I might be late." (l. 235-236)

FURTHER PRACTICE

Explain what happened in the past and what will now happen to the characters in the story. Complete the following sentences to explain what you think.

1. Robert should have ....

2. Robert now should ....

3. The police may decide to ....

4. Margaret must have ....

5. Margaret must ....

6. Margaret might (not) ....

7. Robert could ....

8. The girl may well ....

Patricia Highsmith
The Birds
Poised to Fly

Every morning, Don looked into his mailbox, but there was never a letter from her.

She hadn't had time,° he would say to himself. He went over all the things she had to
5 do – transport her belongings from Rome to Paris, settle into an apartment which she had presumably found in Paris before she made the move, probably work a few days at her new job before she found time and inspira-
10 tion to answer his letter. But finally the greatest number of days to which he could stretch all this had come and gone. And three more days had passed, and still there was no letter from her.

15 'She's waiting to make up her mind,' he told himself. 'Naturally, she wants to be sure about how she feels before she puts a word down on paper.'

He had written to Rosalind thirteen days
20 ago that he loved her and wanted to marry her. That was perhaps a bit hasty in view of a short courtship, but Don thought he had written a good letter, not putting pressure, simply stating what he felt. After all, he had
25 known Rosalind two years, or rather met her in New York two years ago. He had seen

her again in Europe last month, and he was in love with her and wanted to marry her.

Since his return from Europe three weeks ago, he had seen only one
30 or two of his friends. He had quite enough to occupy himself in making plans about himself and Rosalind. Rosalind was an industrial designer, and she liked Europe. If she preferred to stay in Europe, Don could arrange to live there, too. His French was fairly good now. His company, Dirksen and Hall, consulting engineers, even had a branch in Paris. It could all be quite
35 simple. Just a visa for him to take some things over, like books and carpets and his record player, some tools and drawing instruments, and he could make the move. Don felt that he hadn't yet taken full stock of his happiness. Each day was like the lifting a little higher of a curtain that revealed a magnificent landscape. He wanted Rosalind to be with him when he could
40 finally see all of it. There was really only one thing that kept him from a happy, positive rush into that landscape now: the fact that he hadn't even a letter from her to take with him. He wrote again to Rome and put a 'Please forward' in Italian on the envelope. She was probably in Paris by now, but she had no doubt left a forwarding address in Rome.

45 Two more days passed, and still there was no letter. There was only a letter from his mother in California, an advertisement from a local liquor shop, and some kind of bulletin about a primary election. He smiled a little, snapped his mailbox to and locked it, and strode off to work. It never made him feel sad, the instant when he discovered there was no letter. It
50 was rather a funny kind of shock, as if she had played a guileless little trick on him and was withholding her letter one more day. Then the realization of the nine hours before him, until he could come home and see if a special delivery notice had arrived, descended on him like a burden, and quite suddenly he felt tired and spiritless. Rosalind wouldn't write him a special
55 delivery, not after all this time. There was never anything to do but wait until the next morning.

He saw a letter in the box the next morning. But it was an announcement of an art show. He tore it into tiny pieces and crushed them in his fist.

60 In the box next to his, there were three letters. They had been there since yesterday morning, he remembered. Who was this fellow Dusenberry who didn't bother collecting his mail?

That morning in the office, an idea came to him that raised his spirits: her letter might have been put into the box next to his by mistake. The
65 mailman opened all the boxes at once, in a row, and at least once Don had

found a letter for someone else in his own box. He began to feel optimistic: her letter would say that she loved him, too. How could she not say it, when they had been so happy together in Juan-les-Pins? He would cable her, I love you, I love you. No, he would telephone, because her letter would have 70 her Paris address, possibly her office address also, and he would know where to reach her.

When he had met Rosalind two years ago in New York, they had gone out to dinner and to the theatre two or three times. Then she hadn't accepted his next invitations, so Don had supposed there was another man 75 in the picture[1] whom she liked better. It hadn't mattered very much to him at that time. But when he had met her by accident in Juan-les-Pins, things had been quite different. It had been love at second sight. The proof of it was that Rosalind had got free of three people she was with, another girl and two men, had let them go on without her to Cannes, and she had 80 stayed with him at Juan-les-Pins. They had had a perfect five days together, and Don had said, 'I love you,' and Rosalind had said it once, too. But they hadn't made plans about the future, or even talked about when they might see each other again. How could he have been so stupid! He wished he had asked her to go to bed with him, for that matter. But on the other hand, 85 his emotions had been so much more serious. Any two people could have an affair on a holiday. To be in love and want to marry was something else. He had assumed, from her behaviour, that she felt the same way. Rosalind was cool, smiling, brunette, not tall, but she gave the impression of tallness. She was intelligent, would never do anything foolish, Don felt, never any-90 thing impulsive. Nor would he ever propose to anyone on impulse. Marriage was something one thought over for some time, weeks, months, maybe a year or so. He felt he had thought over his proposal of marriage for longer than the five days in Juan-les-Pins. He believed that Rosalind Farnes was a girl or a woman (she was twenty-six, and he twenty-nine) of 95 substance, that her work had much in common with his, and that they had every chance of happiness.

That evening, the three letters were still in Dusenberry's box, and Don looked for Dusenberry's bell in the list opposite the mailboxes, and rang it firmly. They might be in, even though they hadn't collected their 100 mail.

No answer.

Dusenberry or the Dusenberrys were away, apparently.

---

1. Another man in the picture: another man in her life.

Would the superintendent let him open the box? Certainly not. And the superintendent hadn't the key or keys, anyway.

105   One of the letters looked like an airmail envelope from Europe. It was maddening. Don put a finger in one of the slits[2] in the polished metal front, and tried to pull the box open. It remained closed. He pushed his own key into the lock and tried to turn it. The lock gave a snap, and the bolt[3] moved, opening the box half an inch. It wouldn't open any farther. Don had
110 his doorkeys in his hand, and he stuck one of the doorkeys between the box door and the brass frame and used it as a lever.[4] The brass front bent enough for him to reach the letters. He took the letters and pressed the brass front as straight as he could. None of the letters was for him. He looked at them, trembling like a thief. Then he thrust one into his coat
115 pocket, pushed the others into the bent mailbox, and entered his apartment building. The elevators were around a corner. Don found one empty and ready, and rode up to the third floor alone.

His heart was pounding as he closed his own door. Why had he taken the one letter? He would put it back, of course. It had looked like a per-
120 sonal letter, but it was from America. He looked at its address in fine blue handwriting; R. L. Dusenberry, etc. And at its return address on the back of the envelope: Edith W. Whitcomb, 717 Garfield Drive, Scranton, Pa. Dusenberry's girl friend, he thought at once. It was a fat letter in a square envelope. He ought to put it back now. And the damaged mailbox? Well,
125 there wasn't anything stolen from it, after all. A serious offence, to break a mailbox, but let them hammer it out.[5] As long as nothing was stolen, was it so awful?

Don got a suit from his closet to take to the cleaners, and picked up Dusenberry's letter. But with the letter in his hand, he was suddenly curious
130 to know what was in it. Before he had time to feel shame, he went to the kitchen and put on water to boil. The envelope flap curled back neatly in the steam, and Don was patient. The letter was three pages in longhand, the pages written on both sides.

'Darling,' it began,

135 *I miss you so, I have to write to you. Have you really made up your mind how you feel? You said you thought it would all vanish for both of us. Do*

---

2. Slit: *fente.*
3. The bolt: *le verrou.*
4. A lever: *un levier.*

5. Hammer it out: *aplatir (la boîte à lettres) à l'aide d'un marteau, lui redonner sa forme initiale.*

you know how I feel? The same way I did the night we stood on the bridge and watched the lights come on in Bennington...

Don read it through incredulously, and with fascination. The girl was
140 madly in love with Dusenberry. She waited only for him to answer, for merely a sign from him. She spoke of the town in Vermont where they had been, and he wondered if they had met there or gone there together? My God, he thought, if Rosalind would only write him a letter like this! In this case, apparently, Dusenberry wouldn't write to her. From the letter,
145 Dusenberry might not have written once since they had last seen each other. Don sealed the letter with glue, carefully, and put it into his pocket.

The last paragraph repeated itself in his mind:

I didn't think I'd write to you again, but now I've done it. I have to be hon-est, because that's the way I am.

150 Don felt that was the way he was, too. The paragraph went on:

Do you remember or have you forgotten, and do you want to see me again or don't you? If I don't hear from you in a few days, I'll know.
                                                              My love always,
                                                                        Edith

155 He looked at the date on the stamp. The letter had been posted six days ago. He thought of the girl called Edith Whitcomb spinning and stretching out the days, trying to convince herself somehow that the delay was justified. Six days. Yet of course she still hoped. She was hoping this minute down there in Scranton, Pennsylvania. What kind of man was
160 Dusenberry? A Casanova? A married man who wanted to drop a flirtation? Which of the six or eight men he had ever noticed in his building was Dusenberry? A couple of hatless chaps dashing out at 8.30 in the morning? A slower-moving man in a Homburg?[6] Don never paid much attention to his neighbours.

165 He held his breath, and for an instant he seemed to feel the stab of the girl's own loneliness and imperilled hope, to feel the last desperate flut-terings of hope against his own lips. With one word, he could make her so happy. Or rather, Dusenberry could.

---

6. Homburg: *chapeau mou.*

'Bastard,' he whispered.

170 He put the suit down, went to his worktable and wrote on a scrap of paper, 'Edith, I love you.' He liked seeing it written, legible. He felt it settled an important matter that had been precariously balanced before. Don crumpled up the paper and threw it into the waste-basket.

Then he went downstairs and forced the letter back in the box, and 175 dropped his suit at the cleaners. He walked a long way up Second Avenue, grew tired and kept walking until he was at the edge of Harlem, and then he caught a bus downtown. He was hungry, but he couldn't think of anything he wanted to eat. He was thinking, deliberately, of nothing. He was waiting for the night to pass and for morning to bring the next mail deliv- 180 ery. He was thinking, vaguely, of Rosalind. And of the girl in Scranton. A pity people had to suffer so from their emotions. Like himself. For though Rosalind had made him so happy, he couldn't deny that these last three weeks had been a torture. Yes, my God, twenty-two days now! He felt strangely ashamed tonight of admitting it had been twenty-two days. 185 Strangely ashamed? There was nothing strange about it, if he faced it. He felt ashamed of possibly having lost her. He should have told her very definitely in Juan-les-Pins that he not only loved her but wanted to marry her. He might have lost her now because he hadn't.

The thought made him get off the bus. He drove the horrible, 190 deathly possibility out of his mind, kept it out of his mind and out of his flesh by walking.

Suddenly, he had an inspiration. His idea didn't go very far, it hadn't an objective, but it was a kind of project for this evening. He began it on the way home, trying to imagine exactly what Dusenberry would write to 195 Miss Whitcomb if he had read the last letter, and if Dusenberry would write back, not necessarily that he loved her, but that he at least cared enough to want to see her again.

It took him about fifteen minutes to write the letter. He said that he had been silent all this while because he hadn't been sure of his own feel- 200 ings or of hers. He said he wanted to see her before he told her anything, and asked her when she might be able to see him. He couldn't think of Dusenberry's first name, if the girl had used it at all in her letter, but he remembered the R. L. Dusenberry on the envelope, and signed it simply 'R.'.

While he had been writing it, he had not intended actually to send 205 it to her, but as he read the anonymous, typewritten words, he began to consider it. It was so little to give her, and seemed so harmless: when can we see each other? But of course it was futile and false also. Dusenberry

obviously didn't care and never would, or he wouldn't have let six days go
by. If Dusenberry didn't take up the situation where he left it off, he would
210 be prolonging an unreality. Don stared at the 'R.' and knew that all he
wanted was an answer from 'Edith', one single, positive, happy answer. So
he wrote below the letter again on the typewriter:

P.S. Could you write to me c/o Dirksen and Hall, Chanin Building, N.Y.C.

He could get the letter somehow, if Edith answered. And if she didn't
215 write in a few days, it would mean that Dusenberry had replied to her. Or
if a letter from Edith came, Don could – he would have to – take it on himself to break off the affair as painlessly as possible.

After he posted the letter, he felt completely free of it, and somehow relieved. He slept well, and awakened with a conviction that a letter
220 awaited him in the box downstairs. When he saw that there wasn't one (at
least not one from Rosalind, only a telephone bill), he felt a swift and simple
disappointment, an exasperation that he had not experienced before. Now
there seemed just no reason why he shouldn't have got a letter.

A letter from Scranton was at the office next morning. Don spotted it
225 on the receptionist's desk and took it, and the receptionist was so busy at that
moment on the telephone, that there was no question and not even a glance
from her.

'My darling,' it began, and he could scarcely bear to read its gush of
sentiment, and folded the page up before anyone in the engineering
230 department where he worked could see him reading it. He both liked and
disliked having the letter in his pocket. He kept telling himself that he
hadn't really expected a letter, but he knew that wasn't true. Why wouldn't
she have written? She suggested they go somewhere together next week-
end (evidently Dusenberry was as free as the wind), and she asked him to
235 set the time and place.

He thought of her as he worked at his desk, thought of the ardent,
palpitating, faceless piece of feminity in Scranton, that he could manipulate
with a word. Ironic! And he couldn't even make Rosalind answer him from
Paris!

240 'God!' he whispered, and got up from his desk. He left the office
without a word to anyone.

He had just thought of something fatal. It had occurred to him that
Rosalind might all this time be planning how to break it to him that she didn't
love him, that she never could. He could not get the idea out of his mind. Now

245 instead of imagining her happy, puzzled, or secretly pleased face, he saw her frowning over the awkward chore[7] of composing a letter that would break it all off. He felt her pondering the phrases that would do it most gently.

The idea so upset him that he could do nothing that evening. The more he thought about it, the more likely it seemed that she *was* writing
250 to him, or contemplating writing to him, to end it. He could imagine the exact steps by which she might have come to the decision: after the first brief period of missing him, must have come a realization that she could do without him when she was occupied with her job and her friends in Paris, as he knew she must be. Second, the reality of the circumstances that he
255 was in America and she in Europe might have put her off. But above all, perhaps the fact that she had discovered she didn't really love him. This at least must be true, because people simply didn't neglect for so long to write to people they cared about.

Abruptly he stood up, staring at the clock, facing it like a thing he
260 fought. 8.17 p.m., September 15th. He bore its whole weight upon his tense body and his clenched hands. Twenty-five days, so many hours, so many minutes, since his first letter… His mind slid from under the weight and fastened on the girl in Scranton. He felt he owed her a reply. He read her letter over again, more carefully, sentimentally lingering over a phrase here
265 and there, as if he cared profoundly about her hopeless and dangling love, almost as if it were his own love. Here was someone who pled[8] with him to tell her a time and a place of meeting. Ardent, eager, a captive of herself only, she was a bird poised to fly. Suddenly, he went to the telephone and dictated a telegram:

270 *Meet me Grand Central Terminal Lexington side Friday 6 p.m. Love, R.*

Friday was the day after tomorrow.

Thursday there was still no letter, no letter from Rosalind, and now he had not the courage or perhaps the physical energy to imagine anything about her. There was only his love inside him, undiminished, and heavy as
275 a rock. As soon as he got up Friday morning, he thought of the girl in Scranton. She would be getting up this morning and packing her bag, or if she went to work at all, would move in a dreamworld of Dusenberry all the day.

When he went downstairs, he saw the red and blue border of an airmail envelope in his box, and felt a slow, almost painful shock. He opened

---

7. A chore: an unpleasant thing that has to be done.

8. Pled: pleaded

44

280 the box and dragged the long flimsy envelope out, his hands shaking, drop-
ping his keys at his feet.

The letter was only about fifteen typewritten lines.

Don,

Terribly sorry to have waited so long to answer your letter, but
285 *it's been one thing after another here. Only today got settled enough to*
begin work. Was delayed in Rome first of all, and getting the apartment
organized here has been hellish because of strikes of electricians and what-
not.

You are an angel, Don, I know that and I won't forget it. I won't for-
290 *get our days on the Côte either. But darling, I can't see myself changing my*
life radically and abruptly either to marry here or anywhere. I can't possibly
get to the States Christmas, things are too busy here, and why should you
uproot yourself from New York? Maybe by Christmas, maybe by the time
you get this, your feelings will have changed a bit.

295 *But will you write me again? And not let this make you unhappy?*
And can we see each other again some time? Maybe unexpectedly and
wonderfully as it was in Juan-les-Pins?

Rosalind

He stuffed the letter into his pocket and plunged out of the door. His
300 thoughts were a chaos, signals of a mortal distress, cries of a silent death,
the confused orders of a routed army to rally itself before it was too late,
not to give up, not to die.

One thought came through fairly clearly: he had frightened her. His
stupid, unrestrained avowal,[9] his torrent of plans had positively turned her
305 against him. If he had said only half as much, she would have known how
much he loved her. But he had been specific. He had said, 'Darling, I adore
you. Can you come to New York over Christmas? If not, I can fly to Paris. I
want to marry you. If you prefer to live in Europe, I'll arrange to live there,
too. I can so easily...'

310 What an imbecile he had been!

His mind was already busy at correcting the mistake, already composing the next casual, affectionate letter that would give her some space
to breathe in. He would write it this very evening, carefully, and get it
exactly right.

---

9. Avowal: something you admit.

315   Don left the office rather early that afternoon, and was home by a few minutes after 5. The clock reminded him that the girl from Scranton would be at Grand Central at 6 o'clock. He should go and meet her, he thought, though he didn't know why. He certainly wouldn't speak to her. He wouldn't even know her if he saw her, of course. Still, the Grand Central Terminal,
320 rather than the girl, pulled at him like a steady, gentle magnet[10]. He began to change his clothes. He put on his best suit, hesitantly fingered the tie rack, and snatched off a solid blue tie. He felt unsteady and weak, rather as if he were evaporating like the cool sweat that kept forming on his forehead.

He walked downtown toward Forty-second Street.

325   He saw two or three young women at the Lexington Avenue entrance of the Terminal who might have been Edith W. Whitcomb. He looked for something initialled that they carried, but they had nothing with initials. Then one of the girls met the person she had been waiting for, and suddenly he was sure Edith was the blonde girl in the black cloth coat and
330 the black beret with the military pin. Yes, there was an anxiety in her wide, round eyes that couldn't have come from anything else but the anticipation of someone she loved, and anxiously loved. She looked about twenty-two, unmarried, fresh and hopeful – hope, that was the thing about her – and she carried a small suitcase, just the size for a weekend. He hovered near
335 her for a few minutes, and she gave him not the slightest glance. She stood at the right of the big doors and inside them, stretching on tiptoe now and then to see over the rushing, bumping crowds. A glow of light from the doorway showed her rounded, pinkish cheek, the sheen of her hair, the eagerness of her straining eyes. It was already 6.35.

340   Of course, it might not be she, he thought. Then he felt suddenly bored, vaguely ashamed of himself, and walked over to Third Avenue to get something to eat, or at least a cup of coffee. He went into a coffee shop. He had bought a newspaper, and he propped it up and tried to read as he waited to be served. But when the waitress came, he realized he did not
345 want anything, and got up with a murmured apology. He'd go back and see if the girl was still there, he thought. He hoped she wasn't there, because it was a rotten trick he'd played. If she was still there, he really ought to confess to her that it was a trick.

She was still there. As soon as he saw her, she started walking with her
350 suitcase toward the information desk. He watched her circle the information desk and come back again, start for the same spot by the doors, then change

---

10. Magnet: *aimant.*

it for the other side, as if for luck. And the beautiful, flying line of her eyebrow was tensely set now at an angle of tortured waiting, of almost hopeless hope.

355 But there is still that shred of hope, he thought to himself, and simple as it was, he felt it the strongest concept, the strongest truth that had ever come to him.

He walked past her, and now she did glance at him, and looked immediately beyond him. She was staring across Lexington Avenue and into space. Her young, round eyes were brightening with tears, he noticed.

360 With his hands in his pockets, he strolled past, looking her straight in the face, and as she glanced irritably at him, he smiled. Her eyes came back to him, full of shock and resentment, and he laughed, a short laugh that simply burst from him. But he might as well have cried, he thought. He just happened to have laughed instead. He knew what the girl was feeling. 365 He knew exactly.

'I'm sorry,' he said.

She started, and looked at him in puzzled surprise.

'Sorry,' he repeated, and turned away.

When he looked back, she was staring at him with a frowning bewil-370 derment that was almost like fear. Then she looked away and stretched superiorly high on her toes to peer over the bobbing heads – and the last thing he saw of her was her shining eyes with the determined, senseless, self-abandoned hope in them.

And as he walked up Lexington Avenue, he did cry. Now his eyes 375 were exactly like those of the girl, he knew, shining, full of a relentless hope. He lifted his head proudly. He had his letter to Rosalind to write tonight. He began to compose it.

PATRICIA HIGHSMITH (1921-1995)

was born in America but spent most of her life in Europe. She mainly wrote suspense novels and stories which avoid conventional plots, focusing on psychological tension, mood, and the criminal mind. Many of her characters are weak, obsessed or insane and are often totally devoid of any sense of guilt. "She is a writer who has created a world of her own – a world claustrophobic and irrational which we enter each time with a sense of personal danger," wrote Graham Greene.

Novels:
Strangers on a Train (1950)
The Talented Mr. Ripley (1955), the first of several Ripley novels.
Short Stories:
Eleven (1970), a collection of her best short stories.

1 Read the beginning of the short story, down to "a forwarding address in Rome" (l. 44). Go on reading to the end of the passage, even if there are some words or expressions you do not understand. Then answer the following questions.

A. What is the main information you learn in the passage?

Don wrote to Rosalind to tell her:
1. he wanted to live in Europe with her.
2. he loved her.
3. she must write to him.

Don thinks Rosalind has not written to him because:
1. she's too busy.
2. she doesn't love him.
3. she doesn't like writing.

Don is:
1. very happy.
2. depressed because Rosalind hasn't answered.
3. worried about Rosalind.

B. Complete the following chronology to show what happened at the times mentioned.

WHEN?	WHAT?
Two years ago	
Last month	
Three weeks ago	
Thirteen days ago	
From then to the moment when the story begins	

C. List all the elements that, according to Don:

– can explain why Rosalind hasn't answered;

– make this seem strange.

In what other way can her silence be interpreted?

D. Learning to infer

Can the context help you understand the general meaning of the following words?

– stretch (l. 11): ....

– hasty (l. 21): ....

– taken full stock of (l. 37): ....

– forward / forwarding (l. 43-44): ....

2 **Now continue reading, down to "every chance of happiness" (l. 96). Then answer the following questions.**

A. Find out the main information you learn in the passage:

Getting no letter from Rosalind, Don feels:
1. excited.
2. surprised then sad.
3. resigned.

The letters in the box next to his make him feel:
1. jealous of Dusenberry.
2. angry with Dusenberry.
3. that one of them must be for him.

Don thinks that:
1. Rosalind must love him.
2. Rosalind might not want marriage.
3. Rosalind might not be as serious as he is.

At Juan-les-Pins, Don did not ask Rosalind to go to bed with him because:
1. she did not want an affair with him.
2. he did not want to shock her.
3. he wanted marriage, not an affair.

B. Look at the passage again and, in each paragraph, underline one or two sentences which best sum up the main information we learn in the paragraph. Then see if you all agree in the class.

C. List all the elements that might make Don feel pessimistic about his relationship with Rosalind; then all those which show Don's optimism.

Negative elements	Don's optimism

D. What sort of person does Don seem to be so far? Find at least five adjectives (not adjectives from the text) that you might use to describe him.

....

....

....

....

....

3 Now read down to "threw it into the waste-basket." (l. 173) Then answer the following questions.

A. The main information of the passage:

Don breaks open Dusenberry's mailbox because:
1. he's angry with him.
2. he hopes to find a letter for himself inside.
3. he just wants to get a letter – any letter.

Don keeps one of the letters:
1. because it is from Rosalind.
2. because he wants to know more about Dusenberry.
3. for a reason he can't explain.

Don reads the letter and:
1. decides to put it back in the box.
2. tears it up.
3. decides to talk to Dusenberry.

What Don feels for Edith is:
1. envy.
2. love.
3. pity.

B. List all the points you can find which are common to Edith and Don:

– their feelings: ....

– their past lives: ....

– their situation at the moment: ....

C. Learning to infer

The paragraph beginning with "One of the letters" (l. 105) contains a few difficult, more technical words since it describes the way Don opens the mailbox. In the rest of the passage, however, you should be able to understand the meaning of most of the words from the context.

What do you think the meaning of the following words and expressions is?

– pounding (l. 118): ....

– damaged (l. 124): ....

– the envelope flap curled back neatly in the steam (l. 131-132): ....

– in longhand (l. 132): ....

– merely (l. 141): ....

– sealed the letter with glue (l. 146): ....

– spinning and stretching out the days (l. 156-157): ....

– crumpled up (l. 173): ....

4 Now read down to "Friday was the day after tomorrow."(l. 271) and then answer the following questions.

A. The following events take place in the passage. Put them back in their chronological order.

(1) Edith writes him a sentimental letter.
(2) He spends the evening walking in New York.
(3) He sends the letter to Edith.
(4) He regrets not being more open with Rosalind in France.
(5) Don sends Edith a telegram.
(6) He imagines what sort of letter Dusenberry would write to Edith.
(7) Don puts the letter back in Dusenberry's mailbox.
(8) Don realises that Rosalind might not love him.
(9) He tells Edith to send her answer to the place where he works.
(10) He actually writes Dusenberry's letter.

The right order is: ....

B. Don is between two worlds: that of reality and that of dreams, of imagination and fantasy. Using two different colours in the margin of the text, show how the two worlds alternate in this passage.

C. How do you think the story will end? Working in small groups or pairs, imagine an end to the story. Don't write it, simply note down a few points on a sheet of paper. Then tell your stories to the rest of the class. Which endings do you find most convincing / original...?

5 Now read the end of the story on your own.

6 A closer look at language

IN THE STORY

This story is very much about letters and letter-writing, and we see Don constantly thinking about his mailbox. Two letters actually appear in the story. What typical features of letter-writing can you find in each of them?

a. In the letter from Edith (pp. 40-41)

b. In the letter from Rosalind (p. 45)

FURTHER PRACTICE

Write one of the following two letters.

– The letter Don "begins to compose" at the end of the story.

– The letter Edith will write to Dusenberry when she gets back home to Scranton.

... AND FURTHER HELP

Here are a few guidelines to remind you of the layout and common expressions used in informal letters.

	1 25 Richmond Road Kingston upon Thames TW 54 AJD
	2 5 November 1992
3 Dear John,	
4 Thank you very much for...	
5 Looking forward to seeing you soon.	
	6 Love,
	7 Jennifer

1. Your full address (including the postcode).

2. The date. It can be written in different ways:

Saturday, 5(th) November 1992 or November 5(th) 1992 or 5.11.92.
But in American English, the month would come first if you used figures:
11.5.92 = November 5th, 1992.
It is common to omit the year in informal letters.

3. The salutation.

6. The ending of your letter.

The salutation and the end of your letter can be more or less informal depending on how well you know the person you are writing to. Below are the most common expressions used:

	SALUTATION	ENDING
More formal	Dear Mrs Jones	Yours sincerely Sincerely yours Yours truly
More informal	Dear John My dear John	(Yours) affectionately Your affectionate nephew Best wishes Yours (ever) Love Lots of love / Much love

4. The main part of your letter. Here are some standard ways of beginning a letter:

– Thank you for your last letter...
– I'm sorry I haven't written earlier but...
– I'm writing to tell you... / wish you... / apologize...
– I thought I would send you a few lines / drop you a line to...

The first person subject (I / We) and the verb "to be" can sometimes be omitted.

5. It is common practice to use a concluding formula which serves as a bridge between the main part of your letter and the few words at the very end of it. You often allude to the near future in it (plans, arrangements, correspondence, visits...). For instance:

– I am looking forward to seeing you all soon... / to hearing from you...
– My regards to your parents.
– We both hope you can come... / hope these arrangements will suit you...
– I hope everything is going well for you at the moment.
– See you soon. (more informal)
– Don't hesitate to contact me if there is anything I can do.
– I'll write again soon.

7. Your signature.

To help you with your reading

EDGAR A. POE

The Tell-Tale[1]
Heart

True! – nervous – very, very dreadfully nervou
I had been and am; but why *will* you say that
am mad? The disease had sharpened my sense
– not destroyed – not dulled them. Above al
5 was the sense of hearing acute. I heard al
things in the heaven and in the earth. I hearc
many things in hell. How, then, am I mad
Hearken![2] and observe how healthily – hov
calmly I can tell you the whole story.

10   It is impossible to say how first the idea
entered my brain; but once conceived, i
haunted me day and night. Object there wa
none. Passion there was none. I loved the olc
man. He had never wronged me. He had neve
15 given me insult. For his gold I had no desire.
think it was his eye! yes, it was this! He had the
eye of a vulture[3] – a pale blue eye, with a film
over it. Whenever it fell upon me, my blood rar
cold; and so by degrees – very gradually – I made
20 up my mind to take the life of the old man, anc
thus rid myself of the eye forever.

Now this is the point. You fancy me mad
Madmen know nothing. But you should have

1. Tell-tale: which reveals some
information.
2. Hearken!: Listen!

3. A vulture: *un vautour*.
4. Film: veil.

seen *me*. You should have seen how wisely I proceeded – with what caution
– with what foresight – with what dissimulation I went to work! I was never
kinder to the old man than during the whole week before I killed him. And
every night, about midnight, I turned the latch of his door and opened it –
oh so gently! And then, when I had made an opening sufficient for my
head, I put in a dark lantern, all closed, closed, so that no light shone out,
and then I thrust in my head. Oh, you would have laughed to see how cunningly I thrust it in! I moved it slowly – very, very slowly, so that I might not
disturb the old man's sleep. It took me an hour to place my whole head
within the opening so far that I could see him as he lay upon his bed. Ha!
– would a madman have been so wise as this? And then, when my head
was well in the room, I undid the lantern cautiously – oh, so cautiously –
cautiously (for the hinges[5] creaked) – I undid it just so much that a single
thin ray fell upon the vulture eye. And this I did for seven long nights – every
night just at midnight – but I found the eye always closed; and so it was
impossible to do the work; for it was not the old man who vexed[6] me, but
his Evil Eye. And every morning, when the day broke, I went boldly into the
chamber, and spoke courageously to him, calling him by name in a hearty
tone, and inquiring how he had passed the night. So you see he would have
been a very profound old man, indeed, to suspect that every night, just at
twelve, I looked in upon him while he slept.

Upon the eighth night I was more than usually cautious in opening
the door. A watch's minute hand moves more quickly than did mine. Never
before that night, had I *felt* the extent of my own powers – of my sagacity.
I could scarcely contain my feelings of triumph. To think that there I was,
opening the door, little by little, and he not even to dream of my secret
deeds or thoughts. I fairly chuckled[7] at the idea; and perhaps he heard me;
for he moved on the bed suddenly, as if startled. Now you may think that I
drew back – but no. His room was as black as pitch with the thick darkness,
(for the shutters were close fastened, through fear of robbers,) and so I
knew that he could not see the opening of the door, and I kept pushing it
on steadily, steadily.

I had my head in, and was about to open the lantern, when my
thumb slipped upon the tin[8] fastening, and the old man sprang up in bed,
crying out – 'Who's there?'

I kept quite still and said nothing. For a whole hour I did not move
a muscle, and in the meantime I did not hear him lie down. He was still

---

5. The hinges: *les gonds*.
6. Vexed: annoyed.

7. Chuckled: laughed quietly.
8. Tin: *étain*.

sitting up in the bed listening; – just as I have done, night after night, hearkening to the death watches[9] in the wall.

Presently I heard a slight groan, and I knew it was the groan of mortal terror. It was not a groan of pain or of grief – oh, no ! – it was the low
65 stifled sound that arises from the bottom of the soul when overcharged with awe.[10] I knew the sound well. Many a night, just at midnight, when all the world slept, it has welled up from my own bosom, deepening, with its dreadful echo, the terrors that distracted[11] me. I say I knew it well. I knew what the old man felt, and pitied him, although I chuckled at heart. I knew that
70 he had been lying awake ever since the first slight noise, when he had turned in the bed. His fears had been ever since growing upon him. He had been trying to fancy them causeless, but could not. He had been saying to himself – 'It is nothing but the wind in the chimney – it is only a mouse crossing the floor,' or 'it is merely a cricket[12] which has made a single chirp.' Yes, he had
75 been trying to comfort himself with these suppositions: but he had found all in vain. *All in vain;* because Death, in approaching him had stalked with his black shadow before him, and enveloped the victim. And it was the mournful influence of the unperceived shadow that caused him to feel – although he neither saw nor heard – to *feel* the presence of my head within the room.
80 When I had waited a long time, very patiently, without hearing him lie down, I resolved to open a little – a very, very little crevice[13] in the lantern. So I opened it – you cannot imagine how stealthily, stealthily[14] – until, at length a simple dim ray, like the thread of the spider, shot from out the crevice and fell full upon the vulture eye.
85 It was open – wide, wide open – and I grew furious as I gazed upon it. I saw it with perfect distinctness – all a dull blue, with a hideous veil over it that chilled[15] the very marrow[16] in my bones; but I could see nothing else of the old man's face or person: for I had directed the ray as if by instinct, precisely upon the damned spot.
90 And have I not told you that what you mistake for madness is but over acuteness of the senses? – now, I say, there came to my ears a low, dull, quick sound, such as a watch makes when enveloped in cotton. I knew *that* sound well, too. It was the beating of the old man's heart. It increased my fury, as the beating of a drum stimulates the soldier into courage.

---

9. Death watches: death-watch beetles, small insects which make a sound like a watch ticking (and are believed to announce death).
10. Awe: a mixture of terror and wonder.
11. Distracted: bewildered me, made me mad.

12. Cricket: *grillon.*
13. Crevice: crack, opening.
14. Stealthily: quietly, furtively.
15. Chilled: cooled, frightened.
16. Marrow: *moelle.*

95   But even yet I refrained and kept still. I scarcely breathed. I held the lantern motionless. I tried how steadily I could maintain the ray upon the eye. Meantime the hellish tattoo[17] of the heart increased. It grew quicker and quicker, and louder and louder every instant. The old man's terror *must* have been extreme! It grew louder, I say, louder every moment! – do you
100 mark me well? I have told you that I am nervous: so I am. And now at the dead hour of the night, amid the dreadful silence of that old house, so strange a noise as this excited me to uncontrollable terror. Yet, for some minutes longer I refrained and stood still. But the beating grew louder, louder! I thought the heart must burst. And now a new anxiety seized me
105 – the sound would be heard by a neighbour! The old man's hour had come! With a loud yell, I threw open the lantern and leaped into the room. He shrieked once – once only. In an instant I dragged him to the floor, and pulled the heavy bed over him. I then smiled gaily, to find the deed so far done. But, for many minutes, the heart beat on with a muffled sound. This,
110 however, did not vex me; it would not be heard through the wall. At length it ceased. The old man was dead. I removed the bed and examined the corpse. Yes, he was stone, stone dead. I placed my hand upon the heart and held it there many minutes. There was no pulsation. He was stone dead. His eye would trouble me no more.

115   If still you think me mad, you will think so no longer when I describe the wise precautions I took for the concealment of the body. The night waned, and I worked hastily, but in silence. First of all I dismembered the corpse. I cut off the head and the arms and the legs.

      I then took up three planks from the flooring of the chamber, and
120 deposited all between the scantlings.[18] I then replaced the boards so cleverly, so cunningly, that no human eye – not even *his* – could have detected any thing wrong. There was nothing to wash out – no stain of any kind – no blood-spot whatever. I had been too wary for that. A tub[19] had caught all – ha! ha!

125   When I had made an end of these labours, it was four o'clock – still dark as midnight. As the bell sounded the hour, there came a knocking at the street door. I went down to open it with a light heart, – for what had I *now* to fear? There entered three men, who introduced themselves, with perfect suavity, as officers of the police. A shriek had been heard by a neigh-
130 bour during the night; suspicion of foul play[20] had been aroused; informa-

---

17. Tattoo: the beating of a drum.
18. Scantlings: *lattes de bois du parquet.*
19. A tub: a container for a liquid.
20. Foul play: murder

tion had been lodged at the police office, and they (the officers) had been deputed to search the premises.[21]

I smiled, – for *what* had I to fear? I bade the gentlemen welcome. The shriek, I said, was my own in a dream. The old man, I mentioned, was absent in the country. I took my visitors all over the house. I bade them search – search *well*. I led them, at length, to *his* chamber. I showed them his treasures, secure, undisturbed. In the enthusiasm of my confidence, I brought chairs into the room, and desired them *here* to rest from their fatigues, while I myself, in the wild audacity of my perfect triumph, placed my own seat upon the very spot beneath which reposed the corpse of the victim.

The officers were satisfied. My *manner* had convinced them. I was singularly at ease. They sat, and while I answered cheerily, they chatted of familiar things. But, ere long,[22] I felt myself getting pale and wished them gone. My head ached, and I fancied a ringing in my ears: but still they sat and still chatted. The ringing became more distinct: – it continued and became more distinct: I talked more freely to get rid of the feeling: but it continued and gained definiteness – until, at length, I found that the noise was *not* within my ears.

No doubt I now grew *very* pale; – but I talked more fluently, and with a heightened[23] voice. Yet the sound increased – and what could I do? It was *a low, dull, quick sound – much such a sound as a watch makes when enveloped in cotton.* I gasped for breath – and yet the officers heard it not. I talked more quickly – more vehemently; but the noise steadily increased. I arose and argued about trifles,[24] in a high key and with violent gesticulations; but the noise steadily increased. Why *would* they not be gone? I paced the floor to and fro with heavy strides, as if excited to fury by the observations of the men – but the noise steadily increased. Oh God! what *could* I do? I foamed[25] – I raved[26] – I swore! I swung the chair upon which I had been sitting, and grated it upon the boards,[27] but the noise arose over all and continually increased. It grew louder – louder – *louder!* And still the men chatted pleasantly, and smiled. Was it possible they heard not? Almighty God! – no, no! They heard! – they suspected! – they *knew!* – they were making a mockery of my horror! – this I thought, and this I think. But anything was better than this agony![28] Anything was more tolerable than

---

21. Premises: place.
22. Ere long: before long.
23. Heightened: louder.
24. Trifles: unimportant things.
25. Foam: *écumer.*

26. Raved: talked in an excited, uncontrolled way.
27. Grated it upon the boards: pulled it against the boards so as to make a lot of noise.
28. Agony: terrible pain.

this derision! I could bear those hypocritical smiles no longer! I felt that I must scream or die! and now – again ! – hark! louder! louder! louder! *louder!*

'Villains!' I shrieked, 'dissemble[29] no more! I admit the deed! – tear 170 up the planks! here, here! – it is the beating of his hideous heart!'

---

29. Dissemble: hide the truth.

EDGAR ALLAN POE (1809-1849)
was born in Boston and educated in Richmond and in England
after the early death of his parents. He studied at the University of
Virginia, enlisted in the army, but got himself dismissed to start a
career as a writer. He held several jobs as an editor of magazines
and wrote poems and short stories between fits of mental depres-
sion and drinking bouts. He is considered as the inventor of the
modern detective story and is best known for his Gothic horror
stories. They often portray oversensitive characters in the grip of
terror when faced with such supernatural events as vampirism,
spectres, entombments and reincarnations.

Short Stories:
Tales of the Grotesque and Arabesque (1840)

Poems:
The Raven and Other Poems (1845)

Read the whole story, then answer the following questions, looking at the text again whenever necessary.

1 Write down the basic factual information in the following table.

WHO?	The narrator and ...
WHAT?	
WHY?	
WHEN?	
WHERE?	

2 There are three major moments described in the story. What are they?

WHEN?	WHAT?	PAGES / LINES
The first week		

3 Give two main reasons mentioned by the narrator to show us he is not mad.

– ....

– ....

4 Do you think he *is* mad? If you do, list all the points that justify your opinion.

– ....

– ....

– ....

5 The narrator keeps studying the old man, so that the middle part of the text (the second "moment" in question 2) consists of a series of chain reactions. Look at the text again and complete the following diagram.

THE NARRATOR   THE OLD MAN

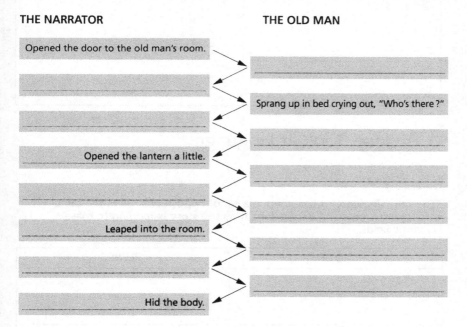

Opened the door to the old man's room.

Sprang up in bed crying out, "Who's there ?"

Opened the lantern a little.

Leaped into the room.

Hid the body.

6 List the expressions showing the increased noise of the beating heart at the end, and the narrator's reactions to it.

The noise of the beating heart:	The narrator's reactions:
–	–
–	–
–	–
–	–
–	–
–	–

7 **Write the police report, beginning as follows:**

At 4 a.m., we arrived at the home of Mr X. The door was opened by a young man who…

8 A closer look at language

IN THE STORY

"The Tell-Tale Heart" is based upon a set of oppositions. Fill in the table below with words and expressions from the story belonging to these semantic fields.

NOISE	SILENCE
LIGHT	DARKNESS
COURAGE / CONFIDENCE	FEAR
RAPID MOVEMENT	MOTIONLESSNESS / CAUTION

FURTHER PRACTICE

Using the blackboard or the overhead projector, write chains of words to try and list / reactivate as many words linked to fear and terror as you can remember. Here is a starting point.

PHYSICAL REACTIONS
(sounds)
You ....
....
....
....

PHYSICAL REACTIONS
(other than sound)
You ....
....
....
....

NOUNS
You feel ....
....
....
....

ADJECTIVES / PAST PARTICIPLES
You feel ....
....
....
....

Isaac Asimov
Robot Dreams

"**L**ast night I dreamed," said LVX-1, calmly.

Susan Calvin said nothing, but her lined face, old with wisdom and experience, seemed to undergo a microscopic twitch.[1]

"Did you hear that?" said Linda Rash, nervously. "It's as I told you." She was small, dark-haired, and young. Her right hand opened and closed, over and over.

Calvin nodded. She said quietly, "Elvex, you will not move nor speak nor hear us until I say your name again."

There was no answer. The robot sat as though it were cast out of one piece of metal, and it would stay so until it heard its name again.

Calvin asked, "What is your computer entry code, Dr Rash? Or enter it yourself if that will make you more comfortable. I want to inspect the positronic brain[2] pattern."

Linda's hands fumbled, for a moment, at the keys. She broke the process and started again. The fine pattern appeared on the screen.

Calvin said, "Your permission, please, to manipulate your computer."

Permission was granted with a speechless

---

1. Twitch: nervous movement.   2. Positronic brain: a type of electronic brain

25 nod. Of course! What could Linda, a new and unproven robopsychologist, do against the Living Legend?

Slowly, Susan Calvin studied the screen, moving it across and down, then up, then suddenly throwing in a key-combination so rapidly that Linda didn't see what had been done, but the pattern displayed a new portion of 30 itself altogether and had been enlarged. Back and forth she went, her gnarled fingers tripping over the keys.

No change came over the old face. As though vast calculations were going through her head, she watched all the pattern shifts.[3]

Linda wondered. It was impossible to analyze a pattern without at least 35 a hand-held computer, yet the Old Woman simply started. Did she have a computer implanted in her skull? Or was it her brain which, for decades, had done nothing but devise, study and analyze the positronic brain patterns. Did she grasp such a pattern the way Mozart grasped[4] the notation of a symphony?

Finally Calvin said, "What is it you have done, Rash?"

40 Linda said, a little abashed, "I made use of fractal geometry."

"I gathered that. But why?"

"It had never been done. I thought it would produce a brain pattern with added complexity, possibly closer to that of the human."

"Was anyone consulted? Was this all on your own?"

45 "I did not consult. It was on my own."

Calvin's faded eyes looked long at the young woman.

"You had no right. Rash your name; rash[5] your nature. Who are you not to ask? *I* myself, I, Susan Calvin, would have discussed this."

"I was afraid I would be stopped."

50 "You certainly would have been."

"*Am* I," her voice caught, even as she strove to hold it firm, "going to be fired?"

"Quite possibly," said Calvin. "Or you might be promoted. It depends on what I think when I am through."

55 "Are you going to dismantle El –" she had almost said the name, which would have reactivated the robot and been one more mistake. She could not afford another mistake, if it wasn't already too late to afford anything at all. "Are you going to dismantle the robot?"

She was suddenly aware, with some shock, that the Old Woman had 60 an electron gun in the pocket of her smock. Dr Calvin had come prepared for just that.

---

3. Shifts: changes.
4. Grasp: understand.

5. Rash: impulsive, hasty.

"We'll see," said Calvin. "The robot may prove too valuable to dismantle."

"But how can it dream?"

"You've made a positronic brain pattern remarkably like that of a human brain. Human brains must dream to reorganize, to get rid, periodically, of knots and snarls.[6] Perhaps so must this robot, and for the same reason. Have you asked him what he has dreamed?"

"No, I sent for you as soon as he said he had dreamed. I would deal with this matter no further on my own, after that."

"Ah!" A very small smile passed over Calvin's face. "There are limits beyond which your folly will not carry you. I am glad of that. In fact, I am relieved. And now let us together see what we can find out."

She said, sharply, "Elvex."

The robot's head turned towards her smoothly. "Yes, Dr Calvin?"

"How do you know you have dreamed?"

"It is at night, when it is dark, Dr Calvin," said Elvex, "and there is suddenly light, although I can see no cause for the appearance of light. I see things that have no connection with what I conceive of as reality. I hear things. I react oddly. In searching my vocabulary for words to express what was happening, I came across the word 'dream.' Studying its meaning I finally came to the conclusion I was dreaming."

"How did you come to have 'dream' in your vocabulary, I wonder."

Linda said, quickly, waving the robot silent, "I gave him a human-style vocabulary. I thought –"

"You really thought," said Calvin. "I'm amazed."

"I thought he would need the verb. You know, 'I never dreamed that –' Something like that."

Calvin said, "How often have you dreamed, Elvex?"

"Every night, Dr Calvin, since I have become aware of my existence."

"Ten nights," interposed Linda, anxiously, "but Elvex only told me of it this morning."

"Why only this morning, Elvex?"

"It was not until this morning, Dr Calvin, that I was convinced that I was dreaming. Till then, I had thought there was a flaw[7] in my positronic brain pattern, but I could not find one. Finally, I decided it was a dream."

"And what do you dream?"

---

6. Knots and snarls: problems.   7. A flaw: an error.

"I dream always very much the same dream, Dr Calvin. Little details are different, but always it seems to me that I see a large panorama in which robots are working."

"Robots, Elvex? And human beings, also?"

"I see no human beings in the dream, Dr Calvin. Not at first. Only robots."

"What are they doing, Elvex?"

"They are working, Dr Calvin. I see some mining in the depths of the earth, and some laboring in heat and radiation. I see some in factories and some undersea."

Calvin turned to Linda. "Elvex is only ten days old, and I'm sure he has not left the testing station. How does he know of robots in such detail?"

Linda looked in the direction of a chair as though she longed to sit down, but the Old Woman was standing and that meant Linda had to stand also. She said, faintly, "It seemed to me important that he know about robotics and its place in the world. It was my thought that he would be par-ticularly adapted to play the part of overseer[8] with his – his new brain."

"His fractal brain?"

Calvin nodded and turned back to the robot. "You saw all this – undersea, and underground, and aboveground – and space, too, I im-agine."

"I also saw robots working in space," said Elvex. "It was that I saw all this, with the details forever changing as I glanced from place to place that made me realize that what I saw was not in accord with reality and led me to the conclusion, finally, that I was dreaming."

"What else did you see, Elvex?"

"I saw that all the robots were bowed down with toil[9] and affliction, that all were weary of responsibility and care, and I wished them to rest."

Calvin said, "But robots are not bowed down, they are not weary, they need no rest."

"So it is in reality, Dr Calvin. I speak of my dream, however. In my dream, it seemed to me that robots must protect their own existence."

Calvin said, "Are you quoting the Third Law of Robotics?"

"I am, Dr Calvin."

"But you quote it in incomplete fashion. The Third Law is 'A robot must protect its own existence as long as such protection does not conflict with the First or Second Law.'"

---

8. Overseer: someone who supervises workers.   9. Toil: hard work.

"Yes, Dr Calvin. That is the Third Law in reality, but in my dream, the Law ended with the word 'existence.' There was no mention of the First or Second Law."

"Yet both exist, Elvex. The Second Law, which takes precedence over
140 the Third is 'A robot must obey the orders given it by human beings except where such orders conflict with the First Law.' Because of this, robots obey orders. They do the work you see them do, and they do it readily and without trouble. They are not bowed down; they are not weary."

"So it is in reality, Dr Calvin. I speak of my dream."

145 "And the First Law, Elvex, which is the most important of all, is 'A robot may not injure a human being, or, through inaction, allow a human being to come to harm.'"

"Yes, Dr Calvin. In reality. In my dream, however, it seemed to me there was neither First nor Second Law, but only the Third, and the Third Law was
150 'A robot must protect its own existence.' That was the whole of the Law."

"In your dream, Elvex?"

"In my dream."

Calvin said, "Elvex, you will not move nor speak nor hear us until I say your name again." And again the robot became, to all appearances, a
155 single inert piece of metal.

Calvin turned to Linda Rash and said, "Well, what do you think, Dr Rash?"

Linda's eyes were wide, and she could feel her heart beating madly. She said, "Dr Calvin. I am appalled. I had no idea. It would never have
160 occurred to me that such a thing was possible."

"No," said Calvin, calmly. "Nor would it have occurred to me, not to anyone. You have created a robot brain capable of dreaming and by this device you have revealed a layer[10] of thought in robotic brains that might have remained undetected, otherwise, until the danger became acute."

165 "But that's impossible," said Linda. "You can't mean that other robots think the same."

"As we would say of a human being, not consciously. But who would have thought there was an unconscious layer beneath the obvious positronic brain paths, a layer that was not necessarily under the control of
170 the Three Laws? What might this have brought about as robotic brains grew more and more complex – had we not been warned?"

"You mean by Elvex?"

---

10. Layer: level.

"By *you*, Dr Rash. You have behaved improperly, but, by doing so, you have helped us to an overwhelmingly important understanding. We
175 shall be working with fractal brains from now on, forming them in carefully controlled fashion. You will play your part in that. You will not be penalized for what you have done, but you will henceforth work in collaboration with others. Do you understand?"

"Yes, Dr Calvin. But what of Elvex?"

180   "I'm still not certain."

Calvin removed the electron gun from her pocket and Linda stared at it with fascination. One burst of its electrons at a robotic cranium and the positronic brain paths would be neutralized and enough energy would be released to fuse the robot-brain into an inert ingot.[11]

185   Linda said, "But surely Elvex is important to our research. He must not be destroyed."

"*Must* not, Dr Rash? That will be *my* decision, I think. It depends entirely on how dangerous Elvex is."

She straightened up, as though determined that her own aged body
190 was not to bow under *its* weight of responsibility She said, "Elvex, do you hear me?"

"Yes, Dr Calvin," said the robot.

"Did your dream continue? You said earlier that human beings did not appear *at first*. Does that mean they appeared afterward?"

195   "Yes, Dr Calvin. It seemed to me, in my dream, that eventually one man appeared."

"One man? Not a robot?"

"Yes, Dr Calvin. And the man said, 'Let my people go!'"

"The *man* said that?"

200   "Yes, Dr Calvin."

"And when he said 'Let my people go,' then by the words 'my people' he meant the robots?"

"Yes, Dr Calvin. So it was in my dream."

"And did you know who the man was – in your dream?"

205   "Yes, Dr Calvin. I knew the man."

"Who was he?"

And Elvex said, "I was the man."

And Susan Calvin at once raised her electron gun and fired, and Elvex was no more.

---

11. Ingot: mass of metal.

ISAAC ASIMOV (1920-1992),
a Russian-born American, was a very prolific writer of
science fiction. His novels and stories explore the implications
of technological progress for humanity, in a form which is often
close to that of other genres like the detective story.

Novels:
The Foundation Trilogy (1951-53)
The Naked Sun (1957)

Short Stories:
I, Robot (1950)
Robot Dreams (1986)

Read the whole short story, then answer the following questions.

1 Who are the three characters in the story?

NAME	PROFESSION	AGE

2 Here is a list of events mentioned in the story. Put them in chronological order.

(1) Linda sends for Dr Calvin.
(2) Linda gives the robot human-style vocabulary and tells him about robotics.
(3) Elvex keeps dreaming.
(4) Dr Calvin kills Elvex.
(5) Linda uses fractal geometry to make the robot more complex.
(6) Elvex relates the nature of his dreams.
(7) Elvex decides he has been dreaming.
(8) Elvex tells Linda he has been dreaming.

3 What does Susan think of Linda? What does Linda think of Susan? What adjectives would you use to describe each of them?

LINDA	SUSAN

4 The Dreams

1. How many dialogues are there with the robot? ....

2. How much does he reveal each time? How does this create suspense?

a. ....

b. ....

74

c. ....

3. List all the words which show that Elvex dreams of robots as if they were human beings.

....

4. What is Elvex's reaction to the condition of these robots in the dream?

5. How and why did he distort "The Third Law of Robotics"?

How? ....

Why? ....

6. In the Bible (Exodus 7:16), God appears to Moses and asks him to lead the Hebrews out of Egypt where they are oppressed. He tells him to go to the Pharaoh of Egypt and say to him: "Let my people go."
What is the significance of Elvex using the same words in his dreams?

7. Why does Dr Calvin kill Elvex at the end of the story?

5 **"Robot Dreams" is also the title of a collection of short stories by Isaac Asimov. Write a blurb (the text the publisher writes on the back cover to encourage people to buy the book) for the collection, basing it on this particular story.**

6 **Elvex wants to "free" all robots, yet sees himself as a human being in the dreams. Do you consider this a contradiction? Imagine he is given two more dreams before he dies and think of an ending to the "story" he dreams of.**

7 A closer look at language

IN THE STORY

This story is very much about relations of power among different "characters". The following sentences all contain verbs that describe the way one person / thing can relate to another one. Look at these sentences, then complete the table which follows with the verbs from the sentences.

– I <u>wished</u> (the robot) to rest.

– That <u>made</u> me realize that what I saw was not in accord with reality. (l. 121-122)

– A robot may not [...] <u>allow</u> a human being to come to harm. (l. 145-147)

– <u>Let</u> my people go. (l. 198)

VERBS	STRUCTURE
...., ...	+ object + infinitive (without TO)
Lead	
Enable, permit, ..., forbid, advise	
Tell, order, invite, persuade, force, invite, persuade, encourage	+ object + TO + infinitive
Remind, warn	
Would like, would prefer, want, ..., expect	
Ask, beg	
Help	+ object + (TO) + infinitive

N.B.: In the passive, TO reappears in structures with "make".
(e.g. He was made to work harder.)

FURTHER PRACTICE

Using the structures described above, complete the following sentences so as to comment on the short story.

– When she does not want to be heard by the robot, Dr Calvin orders ....

....

– Dr Calvin expects ....

– Linda's work on the robot has helped ....

– She will now be forced ....

– Elvex would like ....

– Dr Calvin will now probably forbid ....

– The new robot they will build will be made ....

and they won't let ....

– The short story warns ....

Notes

ROBLEY WILSON
Thief

(Jigsaw reading)

A

His flight leaves in an hour. To kill time, the man steps into one of the airport cocktail bars and orders a scotch and water. While he sips it he watches the flow of travelers through the
5 terminal – including a remarkable number, he thinks, of unattached pretty women dressed in fashion magazine clothes – until he catches sight of the black-haired girl in the leather coat. She is standing near a Travelers Aid counter,
10 deep in conversation with a second girl, a blonde in a cloth coat trimmed with gray fur. He wants somehow to attract the brunette's attention, to invite her to have a drink with him before her own flight leaves for wherever she is
15 traveling, but even though he believes for a moment she is looking his way he cannot catch her eye from out of the shadows of the bar. In another instant the two women separate; neither of their directions is toward him. He orders
20 a second scotch and water.

When next he sees her, he is buying a magazine to read during the flight and becomes aware that someone is jostling him. At first he is startled that anyone would be so close

25 as to touch him, but when he sees who it is he musters a smile.

"Busy place," he says.

She looks up at him – Is she blushing? – and an odd grimace crosses her mouth and vanishes. She moves away from him and joins the crowds in the terminal.

B

30   The girl runs; he bolts after her. It is like a scene in a movie – bystanders scattering, the girl zig-zagging to avoid collisions, the sound of his own breathing reminding him how old he is – until he hears a woman's voice behind him:

"Stop, thief! Stop that man!"

Ahead of him the brunette disappears around a corner and in the 35 same moment a young man in a marine uniform puts out a foot to trip him up. He falls hard, banging knee and elbow on the tile floor of the terminal, but manages to hang on to the wallet which is not his.

C

First: Find a policeman, tell what has happened, describe the young woman; damn her, he thinks, for seeming to be attentive to him, to let herself 40 stand so close to him, to blush prettily when he spoke – and all the time she wanted only to steal from him. And her blush was not shyness but the anxiety of being caught; that was most disturbing of all. *Damned deceitful creatures.* He will spare the policeman the details – just tell what she has done, what is in the wallet. He grits his teeth. He will probably never see his wallet again.

45   He is trying to decide if he should save time by talking to a guard near the x-ray machines when he is appalled – and elated – to see the black-haired girl. (*Ebony-Tressed Thief*, the newspapers will say.) She is seated against a front window of the terminal, taxis and private cars moving sluggishly beyond her in the gathering darkness; she seems engrossed in a 50 book. A seat beside her is empty, and the man occupies it.

D

Two weeks later – the embarrassment and rage have diminished, the family lawyer has been paid, the confusion in his household has receded – the wallet turns up without explanation in one morning's mail. It is intact, no money is missing, all the cards are in place. Though he is relieved, the

55 man thinks that for the rest of his life he will feel guilty around policemen, and ashamed in the presence of women.

E

He is waiting at the airline ticket counter when he first notices the young woman. She has glossy black hair pulled tightly into a knot at the back of her head – the man imagines it loosed and cascading to the small
60 of her back – and carries over the shoulder of her leather coat a heavy black purse. She wears black boots of soft leather. He struggles to see her face – she is ahead of him in line – but it is not until she has bought her ticket and turns to walk away that he realizes her beauty, which is pale and dark-eyed and full-mouthed, and which quickens his heartbeat. She seems aware that
65 he is staring at her and lowers her gaze abruptly.

The airline clerk interrupts. The man gives up looking at the woman – he thinks she may be about twenty-five – and buys a round-trip, coach class ticket to an eastern city.

F

"I've been looking for you," he says.
70 She glances at him with no sort of recognition. "I don't know you," she says.

"Sure you do."

She sighs and puts the book aside. "Is this all you characters think about – picking up girls like we were stray animals? What do you think I am?"
75 "You lifted my wallet," he says. He is pleased to have said "lifted," thinking it sounds more wordly than *stole* or *took* or even *ripped off*.

"I beg your pardon?" the girl says.

"I know you did – at the magazine counter. If you'll just give it back, we can forget the whole thing. If you don't, then I'll hand you over to the police."
80 She studies him, her face serious. "All right," she says. She pulls the black bag onto her lap, reaches into it and draws out a wallet.

He takes it from her. "Wait a minute," he says. "This isn't mine."

G

The man is at the counter with his magazine, but when he reaches into his back pocket for his wallet the pocket is empty. *Where could I have*

₈₅ *lost it?* he thinks. His mind begins enumerating the credit cards, the currency, the membership and identification cards; his stomach churns with something very like fear. *The girl who was so near to me,* he thinks – and all at once he understands that she has picked his pocket.

What is he to do? He still has his ticket, safely tucked inside his suit₉₀ coat – he reaches into the jacket to feel the envelope, to make sure. He can take the flight, call someone to pick him up at his destination – since he cannot even afford bus fare – conduct his business and fly home. But in the meantime he will have to do something about the lost credit cards – call home, have his wife get the numbers out of the top desk drawer, phone ₉₅ the card companies – so difficult a process, the whole thing suffocating. What shall he do?

H

The wallet is a woman's, fat with money and credit cards from places like Sak's and Peck & Peck and Lord & Taylor, and it belongs to the blonde in the fur-trimmed coat – the blonde he has earlier seen in conversation ₁₀₀ with the criminal brunette. She, too, is breathless, as is the policeman with her.

"That's him," the blonde girl says. "He lifted my billfold."

It occurs to the man that he cannot even prove his own identity to the policeman.

1 Here are a number of keywords in a story you will read later. Look at them, then think of the plot of a story including all these keywords. You can use the words themselves (e.g. running) or closely related words (e.g. hurrying), in any order you like, but you must use all the words / notions. Don't write the whole story, just make notes so as not to forget any element of the plot.

RUNNING – BLONDE GIRL – BUYING A MAGAZINE – WALLET – BLACK-HAIRED GIRL – FLYING – FALLING – THIEF – AIRPORT – PICKING UP GIRLS

Then tell your story to the rest of the class and listen to the stories of others. When doing so, write down the order in which the keywords appear in each story.

2 Here is a story by Robley Wilson called "Thief". Its different parts have been jumbled (from A to H). Read them and decide what the proper sequence is.

1. ....   2. ....   3. ....   4. ....

5. ....   6. ....   7. ....   8. ....

Do you all agree about what the right sequence is? If you do, then explain what actually happened in the story. Is the blonde girl a victim like the man?

3 Working in groups of three, imagine the conversation that takes place at the end of the story between the man, the policeman and the blonde girl. Then act it out in front of the class.

4 Write one of the following.

1. The diary of one of the characters in the story for that day.
2. The article that might have appeared in the local newspaper.
3. The blurb (the text the publisher writes on the back cover to make people want to read the book) for the collection of stories, using "Thief" as an example.
4. Another end to the story by imagining a change in the dialogue in passage F.

5 A closer look at language

IN THE STORY

A. Here are a few sentences from the story. The underlined words are all conjunctions introducing a time-clause. Next to each clause, write SIM (if the two clauses describe simultaneous events, that is to say events that take place at the same time) or SUC (if the two clauses describe successive events).

a. He is waiting at the airline ticket counter <u>when</u> he first notices the young woman. ....

b. It is not <u>until</u> she has bought her ticket [...] that he realizes her beauty. ....

c. He wants her [...] to have a drink with him <u>before</u> her own flight leaves. ....

d. <u>When</u> he sees who it is he musters a smile. ....

e. <u>When next</u> he sees her, he is buying a magazine. ....

f. It is like a scene in a movie [...] <u>until</u> he hears a woman's voice. ....

B. The following sentences from the story contain adverb phrases (groups of words which have the function of adverbs). Without looking at the story, see if you can match sentences and phrases.

a. In the meantime...	... the wallet turns up. (A)
b. In another instant...	... he will have to do something about the lost credit cards. (B)
c. Two weeks later...	... he understands that she has picked his pocket. (C)
d. For the rest of his life...	... he will feel guilty. (D)
e. All at once...	... the two women separate. (E)

FURTHER PRACTICE

Here are six pictures which illustrate a story. Tell the story chronologically, imagining what may have taken place "between" the different moments shown here. You can use the pictures in any order you like.

Then tell your story to the rest of the class and listen to the stories of the other students. When doing so, write down the order in which the pictures were used in each story.

... AND FURTHER HELP

Here are a few adverbs and conjunctions of time which you may find useful when telling your stories.

ADVERBS	
AFTERWARDS – We went to the pictures. Afterwards, we had a meal. **BEFOREHAND** – I had prepared my suitcase beforehand, so I was ready to go. **EARLIER** – Hello, Jane! Did you ring earlier? I'm afraid I was away. **FINALLY** – I hate the idea, but he insisted so much that finally, I agreed. **FIRST** – First, we must get some petrol, then we'll go to the post office. **IN THE MEANTIME** – I'm going out around 7 tonight. In the meantime, I'll try to get some rest. **LATER** – He agreed to join us, but later said he was too busy.	**MEANWHILE** – He kept talking on the telephone. Meanwhile Joan was getting nervous and looking at her watch. **NEXT** – There'll be a buffet, and next we'll dance. **PRESENTLY** (= soon) – They presently understood that they were in the wrong place. **PREVIOUSLY** (= before) – They had previously arranged to meet for lunch. **SOON AFTER** – Soon after they moved to New York, they stopped writing. **SUBSEQUENTLY** – She was arrested and subsequently fined £300. **THEN** – They flew to New York; then they took the bus to Boston.

To check your reading

CONJUNCTIONS

WHILE is used for two simultaneous actions:

– He did the washing-up while I cleaned the car.

AS is also used for simultaneous actions but implies a change:

– As I looked at the painting, I began to realize that...

BEFORE / AFTER

– I'll talk to you after you've done the washing-up.

WHEN is used for simultaneous actions:

– I always feel sad when I go back

or successive actions:

– When I realized what he had done, I was furious.

AS SOON AS

– As soon as I get his letter, I'll ring you.

Notes

KATE CHOPIN
Désirée's Baby

As the day was pleasant, Madame Valmondé drove over to L'Abri to see Désirée and the baby.

It made her laugh to think of Désirée
5 with a baby. Why, it seemed but yesterday that Désirée was little more than a baby herself; when Monsieur in riding through the gateway of Valmondé had found her lying asleep in the shadow of the big stone pillar.

10 The little one awoke in his arms and began to cry for "Dada." That was as much as she could do or say. Some people thought she might have strayed there of her own accord, for she was of the toddling age. The prevailing
15 belief was that she had been purposely left by a party of Texans, whose canvas-covered wagon, late in the day, had crossed the ferry that Coton Maïs kept, just below the plantation. In time Madame Valmondé abandoned every specula-
20 tion but the one that Désirée had been sent to her by a beneficent Providence to be the child of her affection, seeing that she was without child of the flesh. For the girl grew to be beautiful and gentle, affectionate and sincere, – the
25 idol of Valmondé.

It was no wonder, when she stood one day against the stone pillar in whose shadow

she had lain asleep, eighteen years before, that Armand Aubigny riding by and seeing her there, had fallen in love with her. That was the way all the
30 Aubignys fell in love, as if struck by a pistol shot. The wonder was that he had not loved her before; for he had known her since his father brought him home from Paris, a boy of eight, after his mother died there. The passion that awoke in him that day, when he saw her at the gate, swept along like an avalanche, or like a prairie fire, or like anything that drives headlong
35 over all obstacles.

Monsieur Valmondé grew practical and wanted things well considered: that is, the girl's obscure origin. Armand looked into her eyes and did not care. He was reminded that she was nameless. What did it matter about a name when he could give her one of the oldest and proudest in
40 Louisiana? He ordered the *corbeille* from Paris, and contained himself with what patience he could until it arrived; then they were married.

Madame Valmondé had not seen Désirée and the baby for four weeks. When she reached L'Abri she shuddered at the first sight of it, as she always did. It was a sad looking place, which for many years had not known
45 the gentle presence of a mistress, old Monsieur Aubigny having married and buried his wife in France, and she having loved her own land too well ever to leave it. The roof came down steep and black like a cowl, reaching out beyond the wide galleries that encircled the yellow stuccoed house. Big, solemn oaks grew close to it, and their thick-leaved, far-reaching branches
50 shadowed it like a pall. Young Aubigny's rule was a strict one, too, and under it his negroes had forgotten how to be gay, as they had been during the old master's easy-going and indulgent lifetime.

The young mother was recovering slowly, and lay full length, in her soft white muslins and laces, upon a couch. The baby was beside her, upon
55 her arm, where he had fallen asleep, at her breast. The yellow nurse woman sat beside a window fanning herself.

Madame Valmondé bent her portly figure over Désirée and kissed her, holding her an instant tenderly in her arms. Then she turned to the child.

"This is not the baby!" she exclaimed, in startled tones. French was
60 the language spoken at Valmondé in those days.

"I knew you would be astonished," laughed Désirée, "at the way he has grown. The little *cochon de lait!* Look at his legs, mamma, and his hands and finger-nails, – real finger-nails. Zandrine had to cut them this morning. Isn't it true, Zandrine?"

65 The woman bowed her turbaned head majestically, *"Mais si, Madame."*

90

"And the way he cries," went on Désirée, "is deafening. Armand heard him the other day as far away as La Blanche's cabin."

Madame Valmondé had never removed her eyes from the child. She 70 lifted it and walked with it over to the window that was lightest. She scanned the baby narrowly, then looked as searchingly at Zandrine, whose face was turned to gaze across the fields.

"Yes, the child has grown, has changed," said Madame Valmondé, slowly, as she replaced it beside its mother. "What does Armand say?"

75   Désirée's face became suffused with a glow that was happiness itself.

"Oh, Armand is the proudest father in the parish, I believe, chiefly because it is a boy, to bear his name; though he says not, – that he would have loved a girl as well. But I know it isn't true. I know he says that to please me. And mamma," she added, drawing Madame Valmondé's head 80 down to her, and speaking in a whisper, "he hasn't punished one of them – not one of them – since baby is born. Even Négrillon, who pretended to have burnt his leg that he might rest from work – he only laughed, and said Négrillon was a great scamp. Oh, mamma, I'm so happy; it frightens me."

What Désirée said was true. Marriage, and later the birth of his son, 85 had softened Armand Aubigny's imperious and exacting nature greatly. This was what made the gentle Désirée so happy, for she loved him desperately. When he frowned she trembled, but loved him. When he smiled, she asked no greater blessing of God. But Armand's dark, handsome face had not often been disfigured by frowns since the day he fell in love with 90 her.

When the baby was about three months old, Désirée awoke one day to the conviction that there was something in the air menacing her peace. It was at first too subtle to grasp. It had only been a disquieting suggestion; an air of mystery among the blacks; unexpected visits from far-off neigh-95 bors who could hardly account for their coming. Then a strange, an awful change in her husband's manner, which she dared not ask him to explain. When he spoke to her, it was with averted eyes, from which the old love-light seemed to have gone out. He absented himself from home; and when there, avoided her presence and that of her child, without excuse. And the 100 very spirit of Satan seemed suddenly to take hold of him in his dealings with the slaves. Désirée was miserable enough to die.

She sat in her room, one hot afternoon, in her *peignoir*, listlessly drawing through her fingers the strands of her long, silky brown hair that hung about her shoulders. The baby, half naked, lay asleep upon her own 105 great mahogany bed, that was like a sumptuous throne, with its satin-lined

half-canopy. One of La Blanche's little quadroon[1] boys – half naked too – stood fanning the child slowly with a fan of peacock feathers. Désirée's eyes had been fixed absently and sadly upon the baby, while she was striving to penetrate the threatening mist that she felt closing about her. She looked
110 from her child to the boy who stood beside him, and back again; over and over. "Ah!" It was a cry that she could not help; which she was not conscious of having uttered. The blood turned like ice in her veins, and a clammy moisture gathered upon her face.

She tried to speak to the little quadroon boy; but no sound would
115 come, at first. When he heard his name uttered, he looked up, and his mistress was pointing to the door. He laid aside the great, soft fan, and obediently stole away, over the polished floor, on his bare tiptoes.

She stayed motionless, with gaze riveted upon her child, and her face the picture of fright.

120 Presently her husband entered the room, and without noticing her went to a table and began to search among some papers which covered it.

"Armand," she called to him, in a voice which must have stabbed him, if he was human. But he did not notice. "Armand," she said again. Then she rose and tottered towards him. "Armand," she panted once more,
125 clutching his arm, "look at our child. What does it mean? tell me."

He coldly but gently loosened her fingers from about his arm and thrust the hand away from him. "Tell me what it means!" she cried despairingly.

"It means," he answered lightly, "that the child is not white; it means
130 that you are not white."

A quick conception of all that this accusation meant for her nerved her with unwonted courage to deny it. "It is a lie; it is not true, I am white! Look at my hair, it is brown; and my eyes are gray, Armand, you know they are gray. And my skin is fair," seizing his wrist. "Look at my hand; whiter
135 than yours, Armand," she laughed hysterically.

"As white as La Blanche's," he returned cruelly; and went away leaving her alone with their child.

[…]*

---

1. Quadroon: someone who has one quarter Negro blood.
* The end of the story has been taken out. See question 3 page 94.

KATE CHOPIN (1851-1904)
spent much of her life in St Louis, Missouri, though she also lived
for a few years in Louisiana, where she became familiar with
plantation life and with the Creole, Cajun and Negro communities.
Her local-colour short stories, which show the influence of
Maupassant, often depict the racial prejudices and the passions
which lurk beneath the surface of civilized society.
As for *The Awakening*, its portrayal of a woman who follows her
sexual yearning and rejects the conventions and restraints of
marriage was considered scandalous, was received with hostility,
and banned from the libraries.

Short Stories:
Bayou Folk (1894)
A Night in Acadie (1897)

A Novel:
The Awakening (1899)

1 Here is the beginning of a short story by Kate Chopin. Read it carefully.

2 How do you think the story will end? Why? Draw up a list of all the clues* that seem to point to the ending you have in mind. Explain why in the column opposite.
(* A clue is information that helps you find the answer to a problem.)

CLUES	WHY?

3 Now write the end of the story. Before doing so:

A. Make sure you know exactly what the end of your story is going to be, and begin by writing a list of points you will mention – a sort of synopsis* of the end of the story. You can then break it down into a number of "scenes", for instance:

– Désirée's reaction when her husband leaves.
– A short dialogue between Désirée and...
– Someone comes to visit, etc.

(* A synopsis is a summary or outline.)

B. Look again at the beginning of Kate Chopin's story and list the stylistic characteristics you notice. (How much dialogue and how much narration? Whose point of view – whose thoughts – do we follow?, etc.)

– ....

– ....

– ....

– ....

If you respect these stylistic features, the ending of the short story will seem more natural.

4 When you have written your stories, exchange them with others written in the class, or read them aloud to the other students. Are there similar endings? Which of these endings do you find most unexpected? interesting? convincing? Are they in keeping with the style of the beginning of the story?

W. SOMERSET MAUGHAM
The Verger[1]

There had been a christening that afternoon at St Peter's, Neville Square, and Albert Edward Foreman still wore his verger's gown. He kept his new one, its folds as full and stiff as though
5 it were made not of alpaca but of perennial bronze, for funerals and weddings (St Peter's, Neville Square, was a church much favoured by the fashionable for these ceremonies) and now he wore only his second-best.[2] He wore it with
10 complacence, for it was the dignified symbol of his office, and without it (when he took it off to go home) he had the disconcerting sensation of being somewhat insufficiently clad;[3] He took pains with it; he pressed it and ironed it himself.
15 During the sixteen years he had been verger of this church he had had a succession of such gowns, but he had never been able to throw them away when they were worn out and the complete series, neatly wrapped up in brown
20 paper, lay in the bottom drawers of the wardrobe in his bedroom.

The verger busied himself quietly, replacing the painted wooden cover on the marble

---

1. Verger: a sort of caretaker who looks after the church building.

2. His second-best: not his best gown but the one afterwards.
3. Clad: dressed.

font,[4] taking away a chair that had been brought for an infirm old lady, and
25 waited for the vicar to have finished in the vestry[5] so that he could tidy up in
there and go home. Presently he saw him walk across the chancel,[6] genuflect in
front of the high altar, and come down the aisle; but he still wore his cassock.[7]

'What's he 'anging about for?' the verger said to himself. 'Don't 'e
know I want my tea?'

30   The vicar had been but recently appointed, a red-faced energetic
man in the early forties, and Albert Edward still regretted his predecessor,
a clergyman of the old school who preached leisurely sermons in a silvery
voice and dined out a great deal with his more aristocratic parishioners. He
liked things in church to be just so, but he never fussed;[8] he was not like
35 this new man who wanted to have his finger in every pie.[9] But Albert
Edward was tolerant. St Peter's was in a very good neighbourhood and the
parishioners were a very nice class of people. The new vicar had come from
the East End and he couldn't be expected to fall in all at once with the discreet ways of his fashionable congregation.

40   'All this 'ustle,[10]' said Albert Edward. 'But give 'im time, he'll learn.'

When the vicar had walked down the aisle so far that he could
address the verger without raising his voice more than was becoming in a
place of worship he stopped.

'Foreman, will you come into the vestry for a minute. I have some-
45 thing to say to you.'

'Very good, sir.'

The vicar waited for him to come up and they walked up the church
together.

'A very nice christening, I thought, sir. Funny 'ow the baby stopped
50 cryin' the moment you took him.'

'I've noticed they very often do,' said the vicar, with a little smile.
'After all I've had a good deal of practice with them.'

It was a source of subdued pride to him that he could nearly always
quiet a whimpering infant by the manner in which he held it and he
55 was not unconscious of the amused admiration with which mothers
and nurses watched him settle the baby in the crook[11] of his surpliced[12]
arm. The verger knew that it pleased him to be complimented on his talent.

---

4. Font: *fonts baptismaux.*
5. Vestry: *sacristie.*
6. Chancel: *chœur.*
7. Cassock: the black gown of a priest.
8. Fussed: got excited or annoyed about unimportant things.

9. Have his finger in every pie: be involved in everything.
10. 'ustle: hustle, hurry and fuss (the verger does not pronounce his "h"s).
11. Crook: *creux.*
12. Surpliced: *en surplis.*

The vicar preceded Albert Edward into the vestry. Albert Edward was a trifle surprised to find the two churchwardens[13] there. He had not seen
60 them come in. They gave him pleasant nods.

'Good afternoon, my lord. Good afternoon, sir,' he said to one after the other.

They were elderly men, both of them, and they had been church-wardens almost as long as Albert Edward had been verger. They were sitting
65 now at a handsome refectory table that the old vicar had brought many years before from Italy and the vicar sat down in the vacant chair between them. Albert Edward faced them, the table between him and them, and wondered with slight uneasiness what was the matter. He remembered still the occasion on which the organist had got into trouble and the bother[14]
70 they had all had to hush things up.[15] In a church like St Peter's, Neville Square, they couldn't afford a scandal. On the vicar's red face was a look of resolute benignity,[16] but the others bore an expression that was slightly troubled.

'He's been naggin' them,[17] he 'as,' said the verger to himself. 'He's jockeyed[18] them into doin' something, but they don't 'alf like it.[19] That's
75 what it is, you mark my words.'

But his thoughts did not appear on Albert Edward's clean-cut and dis-tinguished features. He stood in a respectful but not obsequious attitude. He had been in service before he was appointed to his ecclesiastical office, but only in very good houses, and his deportment[20] was irreproachable. Starting
80 as a page-boy in the household of a merchant-prince, he had risen by due degrees from the position of fourth to first footman, for a year he had been single-handed butler[21] to a widowed peeress,[22] and, till the vacancy occurred at St Peter's, butler with two men under him in the house of a retired ambas-sador. He was tall, spare,[23] grave, and dignified. He looked, if not like a duke,
85 at least like an actor of the old school who specialized in dukes' parts. He had tact, firmness, and self-assurance. His character was unimpeachable.[24]

The vicar began briskly.

'Foreman, we've got something rather unpleasant to say to you. You've been here a great many years and I think his lordship and the gen-
90 eral agree with me that you've fulfilled the duties of your office to the sat-isfaction of everybody concerned.'

---

13. Churchwarden: *bedeau.*
14. Bother: trouble, difficulty.
15. Hush things up: keep things secret.
16. Benignity: kindness.
17. Nagging them: irritating them.
18. Jockeyed: pushed.

19. Don't 'alf like it: don't like it at all.
20. Deportment: behaviour.
21. Butler: *majordome.*
22. Peeress: a woman member of the nobility.
23. Spare: thin.
24. Unimpeachable: impeccable.

The two churchwardens nodded.

'But a most extraordinary circumstance came to my knowledge the other day and I felt it my duty to impart[25] it to the churchwardens. I dis-
95 covered to my astonishment that you could neither read nor write.'

The verger's face betrayed no sign of embarrassment.

'The last vicar knew that, sir,' he replied. 'He said it didn't make no difference. He always said there was a great deal too much education in the world for 'is taste.'

100   'It's the most amazing thing I ever heard,' cried the general. 'Do you mean to say that you've been verger of this church for sixteen years and never learned to read or write?'

'I went into service when I was twelve, sir. The cook in the first place tried to teach me once, but I didn't seem to 'ave the knack[26] for it, and then
105 what with one thing and another I never seemed to 'ave the time. I've never really found the want of it. I think a lot of these young fellows waste a rare lot of time readin' when they might be doin' something useful.'

'But don't you want to know the news?' said the other churchwar-den. 'Don't you ever want to write a letter?'

110   'No, me lord, I seem to manage very well without. And of late years now they've all these pictures in the papers I get to know what's goin' on pretty well. Me wife's quite a scholar and if I want to write a letter she writes it for me. It's not as if I was a bettin' man.'[27]

The two churchwardens gave the vicar a troubled glance and then
115 looked down at the table.

'Well, Foreman, I've talked the matter over with these gentlemen and they quite agree with me that the situation is impossible. At a church like St Peter's, Neville Square, we cannot have a verger who can neither read nor write.'

Albert Edward's thin, sallow face reddened and he moved uneasily
120 on his feet, but he made no reply.

'Understand me, Foreman, I have no complaint to make against you. You do your work quite satisfactorily; I have the highest opinion both of your character and of your capacity; but we haven't the right to take the risk of some accident that might happen owing to your lamentable ignor-
125 ance. It's a matter of prudence as well as of principle.'

'But couldn't you learn, Foreman?' asked the general.

'No, sir, I'm afraid I couldn't, not now. You see, I'm not as young as I was and if I couldn't seem able to get the letters in me 'ead when I was a

---

25. Impart: tell.
26. Knack: gift.

27. A bettin' man: a betting man (who bets money on races or games).

nipper[28] I don't think there's much chance of it now.'

'We don't want to be harsh with you, Foreman,' said the vicar. 'But the churchwardens and I have quite made up our minds. We'll give you three months and if at the end of that time you cannot read and write I'm afraid you'll have to go.'

Albert Edward had never liked the new vicar. He'd said from the beginning that they'd made a mistake when they gave him St Peter's. He wasn't the type of man they wanted with a classy congregation like that. And now he straightened himself a little. He knew his value and he wasn't going to allow himself to be put upon.[29]

'I'm very sorry, sir, I'm afraid it's no good. I'm too old a dog to learn new tricks. I've lived a good many years without knowin' 'ow to read and write, and without wishin' to praise myself, self-praise is no recommendation, I don't mind sayin' I've done my duty in that state of life in which it 'as pleased a merciful providence to place me, and if I *could* learn now I don't know as I'd want to.'[30]

'In that case, Foreman, I'm afraid you must go.'

'Yes, sir, I quite understand. I shall be 'appy to 'and in my resignation as soon as you've found somebody to take my place.'

[…]*

One morning when he was there paying in a bundle[31] of notes and a heavy bag of silver the cashier told him that the manager would like to see him. He was shown into an office and the manager shook hands with him.

'Mr Foreman, I wanted to have a talk to you about the money you've got on deposit with us. D'you know exactly how much it is?'

'Not within a pound or two, sir; but I've got a pretty rough idea.'

'Apart from what you paid in this morning it's a little over thirty thousand pounds. That's a very large sum to have on deposit and I should have thought you'd do better to invest it.'

---

28. A nipper: a child (familiar).
29. Put upon: badly treated.
30. I don't know as I'd want to: I'm not sure I would want to.

31. Bundle: packet.

* A passage of the story has been taken out. See question 1 page 103.

'I wouldn't want to take no risk, sir. I know it's safe in the bank.'

'You needn't have the least anxiety. We'll make you out a list of abso-
160 lutely gilt-edged securities.[32] They'll bring you in a better rate of interest than we can possibly afford to give you.'

A troubled look settled on Mr Foreman's distinguished face. 'I've never 'ad anything to do with stocks and shares[33] and I'd 'ave to leave it all in your 'ands,' he said.

165 The manager smiled. 'We'll do everything. All you'll have to do next time you come in is just to sign the transfers.'

'I could do that all right,' said Albert uncertainly. 'But 'ow should I know what I was signin'?'

'I suppose you can read,' said the manager a trifle sharply.

170 Mr Foreman gave him a disarming smile.

'Well, sir, that's just it. I can't. I know it sounds funny-like, but there it is, I can't read or write, only me name, an' I only learnt to do that when I went into business.'

The manager was so surprised that he jumped up from his chair.
175 'That's the most extraordinary thing I ever heard.'

'You see, it's like this, sir, I never 'ad the opportunity until it was too late and then some 'ow I wouldn't. I got obstinate-like.'

The manager stared at him as though he were a prehistoric monster.

'And do you mean to say that you've built up this important business
180 and amassed a fortune of thirty thousand pounds without being able to read or write? Good God, man, what would you be now if you had been able to?'

'I can tell you that, sir,' said Mr Foreman, a little smile on his still aristocratic features. 'I'd be verger of St Peter's, Neville Square.'

---

32. Gilt-edged securities: *titres, valeurs sûres.*
33. Stocks and shares: *valeurs, titres.*

WILLIAM SOMERSET MAUGHAM (1874-1965)
was educated in England and in Germany, studied medicine, but
never practised, choosing to begin a career as a writer instead. He
worked as an intelligence agent during WWI. He was a prolific
writer who is now best-known for his novels and especially for
his short stories. Many of them are about British expatriates in
Indian and Far Eastern colonies, where infidelity, intrigue and
murder disrupt the small, socially rigid communities. W. Somerset
Maugham has a gift for portraying human types, whom he
describes with detachment and objectivity.

Novels:
Of Human Bondage (1915)
The Moon and Sixpence (1919)
Cakes and Ale (1930)

Short Stories:
The Complete Short Stories (1953)

1 **In many of W. Somerset Maugham's short stories, there are twists
and reversals in fortune reflecting both the difficulty of really knowing
people and the ups and downs of life.**

This is what happens in the short story called "The Verger", though, as you will
see, part of the story has been taken out (l. 147-150). Read the short story carefully in order to understand what changes take place in the life of Albert
Edward Foreman.

Then imagine what the missing part of the story could be. Write it.

2 **Now compare the different passages written in the class.
For each of them, ask yourself:**

– Can the passage really account for Mr Foreman's change in fortune?

– Is it consistent with the personality presented in the earlier part of the story?

Which of the stories do you prefer? Why?

SAKI

• Fur
• Mrs Packletide's Tiger

Fur

'You look worried, dear,' said Eleanor.

'I am worried,' admitted Suzanne; 'not worried exactly, but anxious. You see, my birthday happens next week –'

5 'You lucky person,' interrupted Eleanor; 'my birthday doesn't come till the end of March.'

'Well, old Bertram Kneyght is over in England just now from the Argentine. He's a 10 kind of distant cousin of my mother's and so enormously rich that we've never let the relationship drop out of sight. Even if we don't see him or hear from him for years he is always Cousin Bertram when he does turn up. I can't 15 say he's ever been of much solid use to us, but yesterday the subject of my birthday cropped up[1], and he asked me to let him know what I wanted for a present.'

'Now, I understand the anxiety,' observed 20 Eleanor.

'As a rule when one is confronted with a problem like that,' said Suzanne, 'all one's ideas

---

1. Cropped up: came up.

vanish; one doesn't seem to have a desire in the world. Now it so happens that I have been very keen on a little Dresden figure that I saw somewhere in Kensington; about thirty-six shillings, quite beyond my means. I was very nearly describing the figure, and giving Bertram the address of the shop. And then it suddenly struck me that thirty-six shillings was such a ridiculously inadequate sum for a man of his immense wealth to spend on a birthday present. He could give thirty-six pounds as easily as you or I could buy a bunch of violets. I don't want to be greedy, of course, but I don't like being wasteful.'

'The question is,' said Eleanor, 'what are his ideas as to present-giving? Some of the wealthiest people have curiously cramped views[2] on that subject. When people grow gradually rich their requirements and standard of living expand in proportion, while their present-giving instincts often remain in the undeveloped condition of their earlier days. Something showy and not-too-expensive in a shop is their only conception of the ideal gift. That is why even quite good shops have their counters and windows crowded with things worth about four shillings that look as if they might be worth seven-and-six, and are priced at ten shillings and labelled "seasonable gifts."'

'I know,' said Suzanne; 'that is why it is so risky to be vague when one is giving indications of one's wants. Now if I say to him: "I am going out to Davos this winter, so anything in the travelling line would be acceptable," he *might* give me a dressing-bag with gold-mounted fittings, but, on the other hand, he might give me Baedeker's *Switzerland,* or *Ski-ing without Tears,* or something of that sort.'

'He would be more likely to say: "She'll be going to lots of dances, a fan will be sure to be useful."'

'Yes, and I've got tons of fans, so you see where the danger and anxiety lies. Now if there is one thing more than another that I really urgently want it is furs. I simply haven't any. I'm told that Davos is full of Russians, and they are sure to wear the most lovely sables[3] and things. To be among people who are smothered in furs when one hasn't any oneself makes one want to break most of the Commandments.'

'If it's furs that you're out for,' said Eleanor, 'you will have to superintend the choice of them in person. You can't be sure that your cousin knows the difference between silver-fox and ordinary squirrel.'

---

2. Cramped views: narrow, small (meaning that these people are not generous).

3. Sables: *fourrure de zibeline, de martre.*

'There are some heavenly silver-fox stoles[4] at Goliath and Mastodon's,' said Suzanne, with a sigh; 'if I could only inveigle[5] Bertram into their building and take him for a stroll through the fur department!'

'He lives somewhere near there, doesn't he?' said Eleanor. 'Do you know what his habits are? Does he take a walk at any particular time of day?'

'He usually walks down to his club about three o'clock, if it's a fine day. That takes him right past Goliath and Mastodon's.'

'Let us two meet him accidentally at the street corner tomorrow,' said Eleanor; 'we can walk a little way with him, and with luck we ought to be able to side-track[6] him into the shop. You can say you want to get a hair-net or something. When we're safely there I can say: "I wish you'd tell me what you want for your birthday." Then you'll have everything ready to hand – the rich cousin, the fur department, and the topic of birthday presents.'

'It's a great idea,' said Suzanne; 'you really are a brick[7]. Come round tomorrow at twenty to three; don't be late, we must carry out our ambush to the minute.'

At a few minutes to three the next afternoon the fur-trappers walked warily towards the selected corner. In the near distance rose the colossal pile of Messrs Goliath and Mastodon's famed establishment. The afternoon was brilliantly fine, exactly the sort of weather to tempt a gentleman of advancing years into the discreet exercise of a leisurely walk.

'I say, dear, I wish you'd do something for me this evening,' said Eleanor to her companion; 'just drop in after dinner on some pretext or other, and stay on to make a fourth at bridge with Adela and the aunts. Otherwise I shall have to play, and Harry Scarisbrooke is going to come in unexpectedly about nine-fifteen, and I particularly wanted to be free to talk to him while the others are playing.'

'Sorry, my dear, no can do[8],' said Suzanne; 'ordinary bridge at three-pence a hundred, with such dreadfully slow players as your aunts, bores me to tears. I nearly go to sleep over it.'

'But I most particularly want an opportunity to talk with Harry,' urged Eleanor, an angry glint coming into her eyes.

'Sorry, anything to oblige, but not that,' said Suzanne cheerfully; the sacrifices of friendship were beautiful in her eyes as long as she was not asked to make them.

---

4. Stole: étole.
5. Inveigle: persuade.
6. Side-track: divert.

7. A brick: a good friend, someone on whom you can rely.
8. No can do: I can't.

95   Eleanor said nothing further on the subject, but the corners of her mouth rearranged themselves.

    'There's our man!' exclaimed Suzanne suddenly; 'hurry!'

    Mr Bertram Kneyght greeted his cousin and her friend with genuine heartiness, and readily accepted their invitation to explore the crowded
100 mart that stood temptingly at their elbow. The plate-glass doors swung open and the trio plunged bravely into the jostling throng of buyers and loiterers.

    'Is it always as full as this?' asked Bertram of Eleanor.

    'More or less, and autumn sales are on just now,' she replied.

105   Suzanne, in her anxiety to pilot her cousin to the desired haven of the fur department, was usually a few paces ahead of the others, coming back to them now and then if they lingered for a moment at some attractive counter, with the nervous solicitude of a parent rook[9] encouraging its young ones on their first flying expedition.

110   'It's Suzanne's birthday on Wednesday next,' confided Eleanor to Bertram Kneyght at a moment when Suzanne had left them unusually far behind; 'my birthday comes the day before, so we are both on the look-out for something to give each other.'

    'Ah,' said Bertram. 'Now, perhaps you can advise me on that very
115 point. I want to give Suzanne something, and I haven't the least idea what she wants.'

    'She's rather a problem,' said Eleanor. 'She seems to have everything one can think of, lucky girl. A fan is always useful; she'll be going to a lot of dances at Davos this winter. Yes, I should think a fan would please her
120 more than anything. After our birthdays are over we inspect each other's muster[10] of presents, and I always feel dreadfully humble. She gets such nice things, and I never have anything worth showing. You see, none of my relations or any of the people who give me presents are at all well off[11], so I can't expect them to do anything more than just remember the day with
125 some little trifle[12]. Two years ago an uncle on my mother's side of the family, who had come into a small legacy, promised me a silver-fox stole[13] for my birthday. I can't tell you how excited I was about it, and I pictured myself showing it off to all my friends and enemies. Then just at that moment his wife died, and, of course, poor man, he could not be expected to think of
130 birthday presents at such a time. He has lived abroad ever since, and I never

9. Rook: *corbeau*.
10. Muster: collection.
11. Well off: rich.

12. Trifle: small, inexpensive thing.
13. Silver-fox-stole: *étole en renard argenté*.

got my fur. Do you know, to this day I can scarcely look at a silver-fox pelt in a shop window or round any one's neck without feeling ready to burst into tears. I suppose if I hadn't had the prospect of getting one I shouldn't feel that way. Look, there is the fan counter, on your left; you can easily slip
135 away in the crowd. Get her as nice a one as you can see – she is such a dear, dear girl.'

'Hullo, I thought I had lost you,' said Suzanne, making her way through an obstructive knot of shoppers. Where is Bertram?'

'I got separated from him long ago. I thought he was on ahead with
140 you,' said Eleanor. 'We shall never find him in this crush[14].'

Which turned out to be a true prediction.

'All our trouble and forethought[15] thrown away,' said Suzanne sulkily, when they had pushed their way fruitlessly through half a dozen departments.

145 'I can't think why you didn't grab him by the arm,' said Eleanor; 'I would have if I'd known him longer, but I'd only just been introduced. It's nearly four now, we'd better have tea.'

Some days later Suzanne rang Eleanor up on the telephone.

'Thank you very much for the photograph frame. It was just what I
150 wanted. Very good of you. I say, do you know what that Kneyght person has given me? Just what you said he would – a wretched fan. What? Oh, yes, quite a good enough fan in its way, but still…'

'You must come and see what he's given me,' came in Eleanor's voice over the 'phone.

155 'You! Why should he give you anything?'

'Your cousin appears to be one of those rare people of wealth who take a pleasure in giving good presents,' came the reply.

'I wondered why he was so anxious to know where she lived,' snapped Suzanne to herself as she rang off.

160 A cloud has arisen between the friendships of the two young women; as far as Eleanor is concerned the cloud has a silver-fox lining[16].

---

14. Crush: crowd.
15. Forethought: *préparations*.

16. A silver-fox lining: a play on words, based on the proverb: "Every cloud has a silver lining" (*À quelque chose malheur est bon*).

Mrs Packletide's Tiger

It was Mrs Packletide's pleasure and intention that she should shoot a tiger. Not that the lust[1] to kill had suddenly descended on her, or that she felt that she would leave India safer and more wholesome[2] than she had found it, with one fraction less of wild beast per million of inhabitants. The compelling motive for her sudden deviation towards the footsteps of Nimrod[3] was the fact that Loona Bimberton had recently been carried eleven miles in an aeroplane by an Algerian aviator, and talked of nothing else; only a personally procured tiger-skin and a heavy harvest[4] of Press photographs could successfully counter that sort of thing. Mrs Packletide had already
arranged in her mind the lunch she would give at her house in Curzon Street, ostensibly in Loona Bimberton's honour, with a tiger-skin rug occupying most of the foreground and all of the conversation. She had also already designed in her mind the tiger-claw brooch[5] that she was going to give Loona Bimberton on her next birthday. In a world that is supposed to
be chiefly swayed[6] by hunger and by love Mrs Packletide was an exception; her movements and motives were largely governed by dislike of Loona Bimberton.

Circumstances proved propitious. Mrs Packletide had offered a thousand rupees for the opportunity of shooting a tiger without overmuch risk
or exertion, and it so happened that a neighbouring village could boast[7] of being the favoured rendezvous of an animal of respectable antecedents, which had been driven by the increasing infirmities of age to abandon game-killing and confine its appetite to the smaller domestic animals. The prospect of earning the thousand rupees had stimulated the sporting and
commercial instinct of the villagers; children were posted night and day on the outskirts of the local jungle to head the tiger back in the unlikely event of his attempting to roam away to fresh hunting-grounds, and the cheaper kinds of goats were left about with elaborate carelessness to keep him satisfied with his present quarters. The one great anxiety was lest he should
die of old age before the date appointed for the memsahib's[8] shoot. Mothers carrying their babies home through the jungle after the day's work

---

1. Lust: desire.
2. Wholesome: healthy.
3. Nimrod: a hunter mentioned.
4. Harvest: collection.

5. Brooch: *broche*.
6. Swayed: determined.
7. Boast: be proud of.
8. Memsahib: a European married woman in India.

in the fields hushed[9] their singing lest they might curtail[10] the restful sleep of the venerable herd-robber[11].

The great night duly arrived, moonlit and cloudless. A platform had been constructed in a comfortable and conveniently placed tree, and thereon[12] crouched Mrs Packletide and her paid companion, Miss Mebbin. A goat, gifted with a particularly persistent bleat[13], such as even a partially deaf tiger might be reasonably expected to hear on a still night, was tethered[14] at the correct distance. With an accurately sighted rifle and a thumb-nail[15] pack of patience cards the sportswoman awaited the coming of the quarry[16].

'I suppose we are in some danger?' said Miss Mebbin.

She was not actually nervous about the wild beast, but she had a morbid dread of performing an atom more service than she had been paid for. 'Nonsense,' said Mrs Packletide; 'it's a very old tiger. It couldn't spring up here even if it wanted to.'

'If it's an old tiger I think you ought to get it cheaper. A thousand rupees is a lot of money.'

Louisa Mebbin adopted a protective elder-sister attitude towards money in general, irrespective of nationality or denomination[17]. Her energetic intervention had saved many a rouble from dissipating itself in tips in some Moscow hotel, and francs and centimes clung to her instinctively under circumstances which would have driven them headlong from[18] less sympathetic hands. Her speculations as to the market depreciation of tiger remnants were cut short by the appearance on the scene of the animal itself. As soon as it caught sight of the tethered goat it lay flat on the earth, seemingly less from a desire to take advantage of all available cover than for the purpose of snatching a short rest before commencing the grand attack.

'I believe it's ill,' said Louisa Mebbin, loudly in Hindustani, for the benefit of the village headman, who was in ambush in a neighbouring tree.

'Hush!' said Mrs Packletide, and at that moment the tiger commenced ambling[19] towards his victim.

'Now, now!' urged Miss Mebbin with some excitement; 'if he doesn't touch the goat we needn't pay for it.' (The bait[20] was an extra.)

---

9. Hushed: quietened.
10. Curtail: reduce, put an end to.
11. Herd-robber: the tiger (which robbed herds of their animals).
12. Thereon: on it.
13. Bleat: the noise made by a goat.
14. Tethered: tied, attached.

15. Thumb-nail: very small.
16. The quarry: the animal which is hunted.
17. Denomination: religion.
18. Driven them headlong from: driven them immediately away from.
19. Ambling: walking slowly.
20. The bait: l'appât.

65 The rifle flashed out with a loud report, and the great tawny beast sprang to one side and then rolled over in the stillness of death. In a moment a crowd of excited natives had swarmed on to the scene, and their shouting speedily carried the glad news to the village, where a thumping of tom-toms took up the chorus of triumph. And their triumph and rejoi-
70 cing found a ready echo in the heart of Mrs Packletide; already that luncheon-party in Curzon Street seemed immeasurably nearer.

It was Louisa Mebbin who drew attention to the fact that the goat was in death-throes[21] from a mortal bullet-wound, while no trace of the rifle's deadly work could be found on the tiger. Evidently the wrong animal
75 had been hit, and the beast of prey had succumbed to heart-failure, caused by the sudden report of the rifle, accelerated by senile decay. Mrs Packletide was pardonably annoyed at the discovery; but, at any rate, she was the possessor of a dead tiger, and the villagers, anxious for their thousand rupees, gladly connived at the fiction[22] that she had shot the beast. And Miss
80 Mebbin was a paid companion. Therefore did Mrs Packletide face the cameras with a light heart, and her pictured fame reached from the pages of the *Texas Weekly Snapshot* to the illustrated Monday supplement of the *Novoe Vremya*. As for Loona Bimberton, she refused to look at an illustrated paper for weeks, and her letter of thanks for the gift of a tiger-claw
85 brooch was a model of repressed emotions. The luncheon-party she declined; there are limits beyond which repressed emotions become dangerous.

From Curzon Street the tiger-skin rug travelled down to the Manor House, and was duly inspected and admired by the county, and it seemed a
90 fitting and appropriate thing when Mrs Packletide went to the County Costume Ball in the character of Diana. She refused to fall in[23], however, with Clovis's[24] tempting suggestion of a primeval dance party, at which every one should wear the skins of beasts they had recently slain. 'I should be in rather a Baby Bunting condition,' confessed Clovis, 'with a miserable rabbit-skin or
95 two to wrap up in, but then,' he added, with a rather malicious glance at Diana's proportions, 'my figure is quite as good as that Russian dancing boy's.'

'How amused every one would be if they knew what really happened,' said Louisa Mebbin a few days after the ball.
100 'What do you mean?' asked Mrs Packletide quickly.

---

21. In death-throes: dying.
22. Connived at the fiction: agreed to accept the fiction.

23. Fall in: accept.
24. Clovis: a friend of Mrs Packletide.

112

'How you shot the goat and frightened the tiger to death,' said Miss Mebbin, with her disagreeably pleasant laugh.

'No one would believe it,' said Mrs Packletide, her face changing colour as rapidly as though it were going through a book of patterns before post-time[25].

'Loona Bimberton would,' said Miss Mebbin. Mrs Packletide's face settled on an unbecoming[26] shade of greenish white.

'You surely wouldn't give me away[27]?' she asked.

'I've seen a week-end cottage near Dorking that I should rather like to buy,' said Miss Mebbin with seeming irrelevance. 'Six hundred and eighty, freehold. Quite a bargain, only I don't happen to have the money.'

Louisa Mebbin's pretty week-end cottage, christened by her 'Les Fauves,' and gay in summer-time with its garden borders of tiger-lilies, is the wonder and admiration of her friends.

'It is a marvel how Louisa manages to do it,' is the general verdict.

Mrs Packletide indulges in no more big-game shooting.

'The incidental[28] expenses are so heavy,' she confides to inquiring friends.

---

25. Going through a book of patterns before post-time: this is the image of a woman going through a catalogue of materials (for a dress for instance) because she wants to place an order.

26. Unbecoming: unattractive.
27. Give me away: reveal the truth about what I did.
28. Incidental: supplementary, secondary.

SAKI is the pseudonym of H. H. Munro (1870-1916)
who is chiefly remembered for his short stories. He first worked as a political journalist in Russia and France, then, at the beginning of WWI, lied about his age in order to enlist. He was killed in battle. With wit and sometimes savagery, Saki's stories satirize the conventional Edwardian upper-class society in which they are set. Many of them show sympathy for children and describe the way they play on the feelings of adults, not without malice sometimes.
Saki's best-known collection of short stories is *The Chronicles of Clovis* (1912).

1 Read the two short stories by Saki.

2 You are going to write another story "à la Saki", that is to say in the style of Saki. In order to do that, you need to study carefully the points common to the two stories.

A. What points can you find that are common to the two plots? Think of as many as you can, then fill in the following diagram to show the similarities.

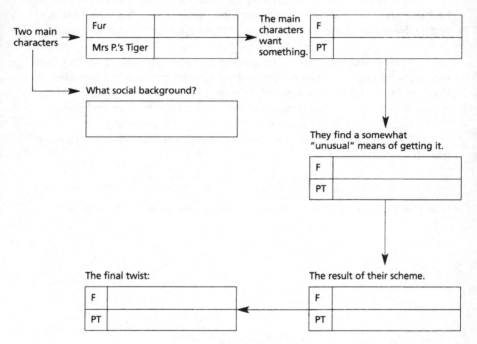

Two main characters →

Fur	
Mrs P.'s Tiger	

→ What social background?

The main characters want something.

F	
PT	

They find a somewhat "unusual" means of getting it.

F	
PT	

The result of their scheme.

F	
PT	

The final twist:

F	
PT	

B. What type of characters do we mainly find in the two stories? Decide which adjectives best describe them (at least the main characters) and justify your opinion.

jealous – kind – honest – greedy – deceitful – generous – ambitious – shy – innocent – selfish – cunning – modest

C. Does anything strike you about Saki's style? List some of its characteristics.

3 **Now think about the plot of your own story "à la Saki". In order to do so, complete the following diagram to decide who the main characters will be, where the story will take place, what will happen, etc.**

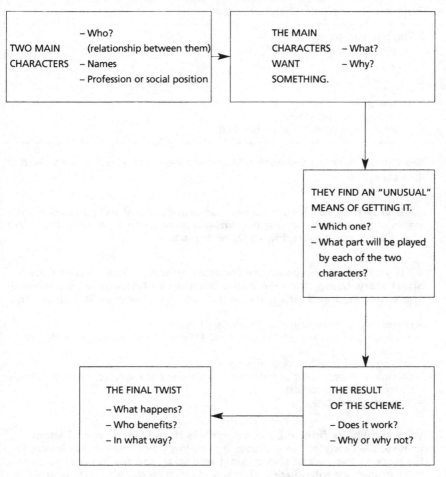

You should end up with as detailed a synopsis as possible, including the characters' names, what happens exactly at each stage of the story, where each part of the story takes place.

You can then decide which parts of the story will be conversation (between which characters?) and which parts will be narration.

4 Then divide your still unwritten story into a number of "parts" corresponding to scenes or narrative parts, and decide what exactly should be mentioned in each of them.

Here is an example of what is required:

The opening scene
- Where?
- When?
- Who?
- What?
- Narrator:
- Dialogue or narration?
- Points that have to be mentioned:

Do the same thing for each of your scenes until you reach the end of the story.

5 Divide the class into a number of groups equal to the number of parts in your story. Each group should now write a passage from the short story corresponding to its own part.

6 If you put all the passages together, you now have a complete short story. Using the overhead projector or photocopies, go through the whole text and edit it (correct it) so as to improve it. This means:

- correcting grammatical and vocabulary mistakes;
- getting rid of inconsistencies between different parts written by different groups;
- adding transitions between the parts;
- changing tenses, point of view, etc., whenever necessary, to make the story clearer and more logical;
- improving the style.

When you have finished, ask yourselves if you can now and again imitate Saki's style, for instance by adding a few humorous touches. Go back to the text of the original two short stories in order to see how points are introduced, characters described, events related so as to be able to imitate some of these techniques.

Notes

KURT VONNEGUT

Next Door

The old house was divided into two dwellings by a thin wall that passed on, with high fidelity, sounds on either side. On the north side were the Leonards. On the south side were the Hargers.

The Leonards – husband, wife, and eight-year-old son – had just moved in. And, aware of the wall, they kept their voices down as they argued in a friendly way as to whether or not the boy, Paul, was old enough to be left alone for the evening.

'Shhhhh!' said Paul's father.

'Was I shouting?' said his mother. 'I was talking in a perfectly normal tone.'

'If I could hear Harger pulling a cork, he can certainly hear you,' said his father.

'I didn't say anything I'd be ashamed to have anybody hear,' said Mrs. Leonard.

'You called Paul a baby,' said Mr. Leonard. 'That certainly embarrasses Paul – and it embarrasses me.'

'It's just a way of talking,' she said.

'It's a way we've got to stop,' he said. 'And we can stop treating him like a baby, too – *tonight*. We simply shake his hand, walk out, and go to the movie.' He turned to Paul. 'You're not afraid – are you boy?'

'I'll be all right,' said Paul. He was very tall for his age, and thin, and had a soft, sleepy, radiant sweetness engendered by his mother. 'I'm fine.'

'Damn right!' said his father, clouting him on the back. 'It'll be an adventure.'

'I'd feel better about this adventure, if we could get a sitter,' said his mother.

'If it's going to spoil the picture for you,' said his father, 'let's take him with us.'

Mrs. Leonard was shocked. 'Oh – it isn't for children.'

'I don't care,' said Paul amiably. The why of their not wanting him to see certain movies, certain magazines, certain books, certain television shows was a mystery he respected – even relished a little.

'It wouldn't kill him to see it,' said his father.

'You *know* what it's about,' she said.

'What *is* it about?' said Paul innocently.

Mrs. Leonard looked to her husband for help, and got none. 'It's about a girl who chooses her friends unwisely,' she said.

'Oh,' said Paul. 'That doesn't sound very interesting.'

'Are we going, or aren't we? said Mr. Leonard impatiently. The show starts in ten minutes.'

Mrs. Leonard bit her lip. 'All right!' she said bravely. 'You lock the windows and the back door, and I'll write down the telephone numbers for the police and the fire department and the theater and Dr. Failey.' She turned to Paul. 'You *can* dial, can't you, dear?'

'He's been dialing for years!' cried Mr. Leonard.

'Ssssssh! said Mrs. Leonard.

'Sorry,' Mr. Leonard bowed to the wall. 'My apologies.'

'Paul, dear,' said Mrs. Leonard, 'what are you going to do while we're gone?'

'Oh – look through my microscope, I guess,' said Paul.

'You're not going to be looking at germs, are you?' she said.

'Nope – just hair, sugar, pepper, stuff like that,' said Paul.

His mother frowned judiciously. 'I think that would be all right, don't you?' she said to Mr. Leonard.

'Fine!' said Mr. Leonard. 'Just as long as the pepper doesn't make him sneeze!'

'I'll be careful,' said Paul.

65   Mr. Leonard winced. 'Shhhhh!' he said.

Soon after Paul's parents left, the radio in the Harger apartment went on. It was on softly at first – so softly that Paul, looking through his microscope on the living room coffee table, couldn't make out the announcer's words. The music was frail and dissonant – unidentifiable.

70   Gamely,[1] Paul tried to listen to the music rather than to the man and woman who were fighting.

Paul squinted through the eyepiece of his microscope at a bit of his hair far below, and he turned a knob[2] to bring the hair into focus.[3] It looked like a glistening brown eel, flecked here and there with tiny spectra where 75 the light struck the hair just so.

There – the voices of the man and woman were getting louder again, drowning out the radio. Paul twisted the microscope knob nervously, and the objective lens[4] ground into[5] the glass slide on which the hair rested.

The woman was shouting now.

80   Paul unscrewed the lens, and examined it for damage.

Now the man shouted back – shouted something awful, unbeliev-able.

Paul got a sheet of lens tissue from his bedroom, and dusted at the frosted dot on the lens, where the lens had bitten into the slide. He screwed[6] 85 the lens back in place.

All was quiet again next door – except for the radio.

Paul looked down into the microscope, down into the milky mist of the damaged lens.

Now the fight was beginning again – louder and louder, cruel and crazy.

90   Trembling, Paul sprinkled grains of salt on a fresh slide, and put it under the microscope.

The woman shouted again, a high, ragged, poisonous shout.

Paul turned the knob too hard, and the fresh slide cracked and fell in triangles to the floor. Paul stood, shaking, wanting to shout, too – to shout 95 in terror and bewilderment. It had to stop. Whatever it was, it *had* to stop!

'If you're going to yell, turn up the radio!' the man cried.

Paul heard the clicking of the woman's heels across the floor. The radio volume swelled until the boom of the bass made Paul feel like he was trapped in a drum.

---

1. Gamely: bravely.
2. A knob: *un bouton.*
3. Bring into focus: *mettre au point.*

4. Objective lens: *la lentille de l'objectif.*
5. Grind into: hit.
6. Screw: *visser.*

100 'And now!' bellowed the radio, 'for Katy and Fred! For Nancy and Bob, who thinks she's swell! For Arthur, from one who's worshipped him from afar for six weeks! Here's the old Glenn Miller Band and that all-time favorite, *Stardust!* Remember! If you have a dedication,[7] call Milton nine-three-thousand! Ask for All-Night Sam, the record man!'

105 The music picked up the house and shook it.

A door slammed next door. Now someone hammered[8] on a door.

Paul looked down into his microscope once more, looked at nothing – while a prickling sensation spread over his skin. He faced the truth: The man and woman would kill each other, if he didn't stop them.

110 He beat on the wall with his fist. 'Mr. Harger! Stop it!' he cried. 'Mrs. Harger! Stop it!'

'For Ollie from Lavinia!' All-Night Sam cried back at him. 'For Ruth from Carl, who'll never forget last Tuesday! For Wilbur from Mary, who's lonesome tonight! Here's the Sauter-Finnegan Band asking, *Love, What Are* 115 *You Doing to My Heart?'*

Next door, crockery[9] smashed,[10] filling a split second of radio silence. And then the tidal wave of music drowned everything again.

Paul stood by the wall, trembling in his helplessness. 'Mr. Harger! Mrs. Harger! Please!'

120 'Remember the number!' said All-Night Sam. 'Milton nine-three-thousand!'

Dazed, Paul went to the phone and dialed the number.

'WJCD,[11]' said the switchboard operator.

'Would you kindly connect me with All-Night Sam?' said Paul.

'Hello!' said All-Night Sam. He was eating, talking with a full mouth.
125 In the background, Paul could hear sweet, bleating music, the original of what was rending the radio next door.

'I wonder if I might make a dedication,' said Paul.

'Dunno why not,' said Sam. 'Ever belong to any organization listed as subversive by the Attorney General's office?'

130 Paul thought a moment. 'Nossir – I don't think so, sir,' he said.

'Shoot,[12]' said Sam.

'From Mr. Lemuel K. Harger to Mrs. Harger,' said Paul.

'What's the message?' said Sam.

'I love you,' said Paul. 'Let's make up[13] and start all over again.'

---

7. Dedication: a message the radio announcer reads before a piece of music is played (sent by one listener to another).
8. Hammer: knock hard.
9. Crockery: plates and cups.
10. Smashed: broke.
11. WJCD: the name of the radio station.
12. Shoot: start talking (= reading your dedication).
13. Make up: get reconciled.

135   The woman's voice was so shrill with passion that it cut through the din of the radio, and even Sam heard it.

'Kid – are you in trouble?' said Sam. 'Your folks fighting?'

Paul was afraid that Sam would hang up on him if he found out that Paul wasn't a blood relative of the Hargers. 'Yessir,' he said.

140   'And you're trying to pull 'em back together again with this dedication?' said Sam.

'Yessir,' said Paul.

Sam became very emotional. 'O.K., kid,' he said hoarsely, 'I'll give it everything I've got. Maybe it'll work. I once saved a guy from shooting him-
145 self the same way.'

'How did you do that?' said Paul fascinated.

'He called up and said he was gonna blow his brains out,' said Sam, 'and I played *The Bluebird of Happiness*.' He hung up.

Paul dropped the telephone into its cradle. The music stopped, and
150 Paul's hair stood on end. For the first time, the fantastic speed of modern communications was real to him, and he was appalled.

'Folks!' said Sam, 'I guess everybody stops and wonders sometimes what the heck he thinks he's doin' with the life the good Lord gave him! It may seem funny to you folks, because I always keep up a cheerful front, no
155 matter how I feel inside, that I wonder sometimes, too! And then, just like some angel was trying to tell me, "Keep going, Sam, keep going," something like this comes along.'

'Folks!' said Sam, 'I've been asked to bring a man and his wife back together again through the miracle of radio! I guess there's no sense in kid-
160 ding ourselves[14] about marriage! It isn't any bowl of cherries! There's ups and downs, and sometimes folks don't see how they can go on!'

Paul was impressed with the wisdom and authority of Sam. Having the radio turned up high made sense now, for Sam was speaking like the right-hand man of God.

165   When Sam paused for effect, all was still next door. Already the miracle was working.

'Now,' said Sam, 'a guy in my business has to be half musician, half philosopher, half psychiatrist, and half electrical engineer! And! If I've learned one thing from working with all you wonderful people out there,
170 it's this: if folks would swallow their self-respect and pride, there wouldn't be any more divorces!'

---

14. Kidding ourselves: having illusions.

There were affectionate cooings[15] from next door. A lump grew in Paul's throat as he thought about the beautiful thing he and Sam were bringing to pass.

175 'Folks!' said Sam, 'that's all I'm gonna say about love and marriage! That's all anybody needs to know! And now, for Mrs. Lemuel K. Harger, from Mr. Harger – I love you! Let's make up and start all over again!' Sam choked up. 'Here's Eartha Kitt, and *Somebody Bad Stole De Wedding Bell!*'

The radio next door went off.

180 The world lay still.

A purple emotion flooded Paul's being. Childhood dropped away, and he hung, dizzy on the brink of life, rich, violent, rewarding.

There was movement next door – slow, foot-dragging movement.

'So,' said the woman.

185 'Charlotte – ' said the man uneasily 'Honey – I swear.'

'"I love you,"' she said bitterly, '"let's make up and start all over again."'

Baby,' said the man desperately, 'it's another Lemuel K. Harger. It's got to be!'

'You want your wife back?' she said. 'All right – I won't get in her 190 way. She can have you, Lemuel – you jewel beyond price, you.'

'*She* must have called the station,' said the man.

'She can have you, you philandering,[16] two-timing, two-bit Lochinvar,[17]' she said. 'But you won't be in very good condition.'

'Charlotte – put down that gun,' said the man. 'Don't do anything 195 you'll be sorry for.'

'That's all behind me, you worm,' she said.

There were three shots.

Paul ran out into the hall, and bumped into the woman as she burst from the Harger apartment. She was a big, blonde woman, all soft and 200 awry, like an unmade bed.

She and Paul screamed at the same time, and then she grabbed him as he started to run.

'You want candy?' she said wildly. 'Bicycle?'

'No, thank you,' said Paul shrilly. 'Not at this time.'

205 'You haven't seen or heard a thing!' she said. 'You know what happens to squealers?[18]'

15. Cooings: soft, affectionate sounds (the sounds made by pigeons).
16. Philandering: from a philanderer = someone who flirts a lot.
17. Lochinvar: a character in Walter Scott's "Marmion", who is in love with a lady and runs away with her just before her marriage to another man.
18. Squealer: someone who informs the police about a crime that has been committed.

124

'Yes!' cried Paul.

She dug into her purse, and brought out a perfumed mulch[19] of face tissues, bobbypins and cash. 'Here!' she panted. 'It's yours! And there's more where that came from, if you keep your mouth shut.' She stuffed it into his trousers pocket.

She looked at him fiercely, then fled into the street.

Paul ran back into his apartment, jumped into bed, and pulled the covers up over his head. In the hot, dark cave of the bed, he cried because he and All-Night Sam had helped to kill a man.

A policeman came clumping into the house very soon, and he knocked on both apartment doors with his billyclub.

Numb, Paul crept out of the hot, dark cave, and answered the door. Just as he did, the door across the hall opened, and there stood Mr. Harger, haggard but whole.

'Yes, sir?' said Harger. He was a small, balding man, with a hairline mustache. 'Can I help you?'

'The neighbors heard some shots,' said the policeman.

'Really?' said Harger urbanely. He dampened his mustache with the tip of his little finger. 'How bizarre. I heard nothing.' He looked at Paul sharply. 'Have you been playing with your father's guns again, young man?'

'Oh, nossir!' said Paul, horrified.

'Where are your folks?' said the policeman to Paul.

'At the movies,' said Paul.

'You're all alone?' said the policeman.

'Yessir,' said Paul. 'It's an adventure.'

'I'm sorry I said that about the guns,' said Harger. 'I certainly would have heard any shots in this house. The walls are thin as paper, and I heard nothing.'

Paul looked at him gratefully.

'And you didn't hear any shots, either, kid?' said the policeman.

Before Paul could find an answer, there was a disturbance out on the street. A big motherly woman was getting out of a taxi-cab and wailing[20] at the top of her lungs. 'Lem! Lem baby.'

She barged into the foyer, a suitcase bumping against her leg and tearing her stockings to shreds. She dropped the suitcase, and ran to Harger, throwing her arms around him.

---

19. Mulch: mixture.   20. Wailing: crying, howling.

'I got your message, darling,' she said, 'and I did just what All-Night Sam told me to do. I swallowed my self-respect, and here I am!'

245 'Rose, Rose, Rose – my little Rose,' said Harger. 'Don't ever leave me again.' They grappled with each other affectionately and staggered into their apartment.

'Just look at this apartment!' said Mrs. Harger. 'Men are just lost without women!' As she closed the door, Paul could see that she was 250 awfully pleased with the mess.

'You *sure* you didn't hear any shots?' said the policeman to Paul.

The ball of money in Paul's pocket seemed to swell to the size of a watermelon. 'Yessir,' he croaked.

The policeman left.

255 Paul shut his apartment door, shuffled into his bedroom, and collapsed on the bed.

The next voices Paul heard came from his own side of the wall. The voices were sunny – the voices of his mother and father. His mother was singing a nursery rhyme and his father was undressing him.

260 'Diddle-diddle-dumpling, my son John,' piped his mother, 'Went to bed with his stockings on. One shoe off, and one shoe on – diddle-diddle-dumpling, my son John.'

Paul opened his eyes.

'Hi, big boy,' said his father, 'you went to sleep with all your clothes 265 on.'

'How's my little adventurer?' said his mother.

'O.K.,' said Paul sleepily. 'How was the show?'

'It wasn't for children, honey,' said his mother. 'Your would have liked the short subject, though. It was all about bears – cunning little cubs.'

270 Paul's father handed her Paul's trousers and she shook them out, and hung them neatly on the back of a chair by the bed. She patted them smooth, and felt the ball of money in the pocket. 'Little boys' pockets!' she said, delighted. 'Full of childhood's mysteries. An enchanted frog? A magic pocketknife from a fairy princess?' She caressed the lump.

275 'He's not a little boy – he's a big boy,' said Paul's father. 'And he's too old to be thinking about fairy princesses.'

Paul's mother held up her hands. 'Don't rush it, don't rush it. When I saw him asleep there, I realized all over again how dreadfully short childhood is.' She reached into the pocket and sighed wistfully. 'Little boys are 280 so hard on clothes – especially pockets.'

She brought out the ball and held it under Paul's nose, 'Now, would you mind telling Mommy what we have here?' she said gaily.

The ball bounced like a frowzy chrysanthemum, with ones, fives, tens, twenties, and lipstick-stained Kleenex for petals. And rising from it, 285 befuddling Paul's young mind, was the pungent musk of perfume.

Paul's father sniffed the air. 'What's that smell?' he said.

Paul's mother rolled her eyes. '*Tabu,*[21]' she said.

---

21. Tabu: the name of a perfume.

KURT VONNEGUT
was born in Indiana in 1922. During WWII, he was captured by the Germans and interned as a prisoner of war in Dresden. This experience became the subject of *Slaughterhouse-Five*, a novel which deals with the bombing of Dresden in 1945. The story is fragmented and its chronology distorted to render the absurdity and confusion of war. In his other works Vonnegut uses satire, irony, black humour and often science fiction in order to raise questions about modern existence in a world which is increasingly beyond people's control.

Novels:
Cat's Cradle (1963)
Slaughterhouse-Five (1969)
Short Stories:
Welcome to the Monkey House (1968)

Crédits photos

p. 6-7 : *Howards End*, 1992. Dir : J. Ivory. Merchant Ivory Prod. © Prod.

pp. 22-23 : Fuseli

pp. 36-37 : Pennsylvania Station. © : UPI/Corbis-Bettmann/Sipa.

pp. 54-55 : Harry Clarke, from *The illustrated E. A. Poe* ed. by Roy Gasson. New Orchard Ed.

pp. 66-67 : *Metropolis*, 1927. Dir : F. Lang. SIPA PRESS.

pp. 78-79 : *La diseuse de bonne aventure*, G. De La Tour. New York Metropolitan Museum of Art. Ph : Josse.

pp. 84-85 : Ph. F. Grellet.

pp. 88-89 : Ph. F. Grellet.

pp. 96-97 : Frans Masereel, 1922. Offenbach am Main, Klingspor Museum © AKG Paris.

pp. 104-105 : Sir Henry Hesketh Bell. © Royal Commonwealth Society Collection. Cambridge University Library. By permission of the Syndics of Cambridge University Library.

pp. 118-119 : *Night Windows*, E. Hopper, 1928. New York Museum of Modern Art.

Crédits textes

– Roald Dahl *The Landlady* in *Tales of the Unexpected* © Michael Joseph 1979. Penguin Books.
– Tony Wilmot *Skeleton in the Cupboard*. First published in Weekend Extra, reprinted in *Tales of the Unexpected*, Penguin Books, 1988. © Tony Wilmot 1985.
– Patricia Highsmith *The Birds Poised to Fly* in *Eleven*. Heinemann 1970 © P. Highsmith.
– Edgar A. Poe *The Tell-Tale Heart*, 1843.
– Isaac Asimov *Robot Dreams* © I. Asimov 1986.
– Robley Wilson Jr *Thief* in *Dancing for Men*, University of Pittsburgh Press © R. Wilson Jr 1983.
– Kate Chopin *Désirée's Baby* in *Bayou Folk*, 1894.
– W. S. Maugham *The Verger* in *Collected Short Stories*, vol. 2. Heinemann 1951. © The Royal Literary Fund.
– Saki *Fur* and *Mrs Packletide's Tiger* in *The Chronicles of Clovis*, 1911.
– Kurt Vonnegut *Next Door* in *Welcome to the Monkey House*. First published in G. B. by J. Cape, 1968. © K. Vonnegut.

Achevé d'imprimer en France par Dupli-Print à Domont (95)
Dépôt légal : 04/2017 - Collection n° 69 - Édition 19
N° d'impression : 201702979
13/5181/6